Herbert Henry Dow, 1866–1930

HERBERT H. DOW

PIONEER   IN CREATIVE CHEMISTRY

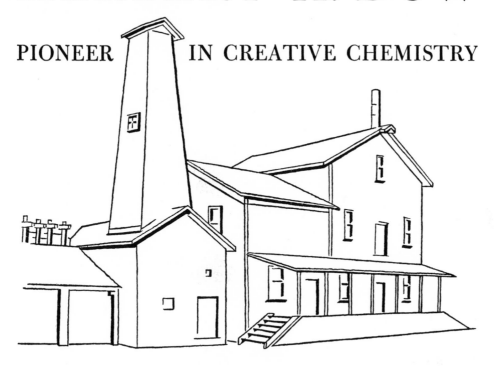

By Murray Campbell and Harrison Hatton

APPLETON-CENTURY-CROFTS, INC., NEW YORK ◆ 1951

FOREWORD

THIS BOOK IS AN ACCOUNT, IN NONTECHNICAL TERMS, OF ONE MAN'S SHARE IN the founding of a company and, in a way, of an industry.

When Herbert Dow built his first little chemical plant, all but a few easy-to-make "work horse" chemicals came from Europe, especially Germany. When he died, forty years later, his company alone was making 800 carloads a month of 150 different chemicals, at least three other American companies were even larger, and, most important of all, this country was free of foreign dominance in matters chemical.

None of this just "happened." It was the result of a long struggle, or rather of two long struggles. One of these was to wrest from Nature chemical secrets which had lain undiscovered since the beginning of time. The other was to stay alive in the face of commercially murderous tactics of rich and powerful foreign combines, who preferred to do all the wresting themselves—at their own price.

Herbert Dow was by no means the only American entry in these two struggles. But he was one of the chief and most picturesque, and this book reveals for the first time just what he did and how he did it.

In preparing this account, the authors were allowed to come in from the outside and assemble and examine many thousands of records and documents, to take hundreds upon hundreds of hours of executive time in search of information and attitudes, and to form and set down the picture as it appeared to them as independent observers.

It is doubtful if any two pairs of hands could, without help, have uncovered and assembled the vast store of detailed information from which the present account stems. The authors gratefully acknowledge the co-operation of all ranks of the Dow organization, from top executives to members of the labor force who knew and worked with Herbert Dow. Especially helpful were Thomas Griswold, H. S. Kendall, F. H. Langell, of the executive staff, and Miss Ruth Perry, secretary to the late Willard H. Dow. It should also be noted that it was Dr. Willard Dow who originally authorized the project, and Dudley L. Parsons who suggested it and laid out the approach.

It has been remarked that corporations, even some as vast in size and scope as the present Dow Chemical Company, are sometimes enlarged reflections of the character and personality of the man who started them. That is certainly so here, and hence the reader may occasionally find himself wondering if he is reading the life story of an American industrialist, the history of a company as he founded and developed it, or the story of a great industry as it came of age in this country. Actually, the three are inseparable, and it is the hope of the authors that their narrative makes the point clear.

M.C. H.H.

CONTENTS

ILLUSTRATIONS

xi

AN INTRODUCTION TO HERBERT H. DOW

HERBERT HENRY DOW, FOUNDER OF THE DOW CHEMICAL COMPANY, AND ONE of the creators of the modern American chemical industry, was born in 1866. As a youth still in college, he became aware of the vast stores of prehistoric brine trapped under the village of Midland, in Michigan. Drawing products useful to man from this brine was to be his lifework. By the time of his death in 1930, the group of small wooden buildings in which he commenced operations had become one of the great industrial plants of the world, supplying directly and indirectly from brine some one hundred and fifty products useful in daily life.

But Herbert Dow's plant, which has since multiplied in size and usefulness, was more than an industrial and technological triumph. Like his life, he made it a symbol of certain native American virtues, which to him seemed very important. One of these was a sort of old-fashioned frugality, expressed in terms of hatred of waste. He began his career in a day when aggressive wastefulness was almost the keynote of many American industries: forests were slashed down ruthlessly, with no thought of where wood was to come from when they were gone; treasures of petroleum and natural gas were squandered with indifferent ineptness; vast prairies were broken up with the plow and abandoned to become dust bowls. Nor was the rudimentary chemical industry of Dow's early days at all guiltless. As a young man, he perfected a process for extracting bromine from brine, and after long struggle built a profitable little company around it. When, however, he suggested recovering also the still more useful chlorine, instead of running it off down the sewer, his backers greeted the notion first with indifference and then with hostility. Dow recovered the chlorine anyway, and built a vast company on it. Had he acceded to the day's indifference to wastefulness, this country might still be relying on other nations for some of its most important chemicals.

1

Another native American virtue strong in Herbert Dow was the spirit of competition—not competition to make unearned millions by financial manipulation, or by inflated claims as to his company's and his products' merits, but competition by bringing his products to market more economically than anyone else could.

"If we can't do a thing better than it's already being done," he used to say, "why do it?"

Herbert Dow believed, too, in the essential dignity of man—a virtue easier to approve than to practice on a large scale. He spent a large part of his time in the factory, and knew most of his workmen as well as he knew his executives. He could not bear to see even his most minor employee imposed on: once he found that one of his workmen had been overcharged for medical care; he took the matter in hand and forced a 75 per cent reduction in the bill. And he was long resented by certain shopkeepers for paying his workmen in cash instead of the usual scrip, which the shopkeepers made a practice of discounting to their advantage. These seem like trivial things nowadays, but they helped make up an attitude to workingmen not common in Dow's early days.

It is not possible to examine in this brief introductory chapter all of Herbert Dow's technological accomplishments in his chosen field of industrial chemistry. That is, in fact, to be the chief task of this entire book. Nevertheless, it is useful here to set down certain leading thoughts, which will develop as his story unfolds.

One is that Herbert Dow did not so much choose the field of the modern American industrial chemistry as help—it might almost be said—to create it. His was certainly not the only company to do this; nor did he accomplish his share alone. He had to an almost incredible extent the ability to imbue other men with his determination to solve chemical and manufacturing problems. Sometimes the solution took months and sometimes it took years; sometimes it never came. Chemistry is the science of rearranging atoms; industrial chemistry is the business of rearranging them by the ton or even the trainload. Often rearrangements that are easily enough made in the chaste glassiness of the laboratory are very hard to achieve in the factory. Sometimes, as we shall see, Dow's ideas took five or even ten years to progress from the laboratory to paying commercial status.

If the translation from laboratory possibility to factory actuality was often slow and frustrating, it can be imagined how hard it was when Dow proposed rearrangements of atoms that Mother Nature simply would not consent to. Sometimes he and his associates found ways around her refusal; sometimes, after years of trying, they had to give up. Herbert Dow was a very determined man, and never gave up an idea willingly. Nothing annoyed him so much as to have an associate decide too soon that something he proposed "couldn't be done."

"I can find a hundred men to tell me an idea won't work," he once said. "What I want are men who will *make* it work."

However, he never blamed anyone if a proposed idea eventually and finally proved to be unworkable. Instead, he would examine the failure for what could be learned from it, and put this knowledge to use on some other idea. Failure, in short, was never able to reach him emotionally, though it more than once cleaned him out of everything but courage—and more ideas. He was, as we shall see, to be frustrated repeatedly, both financially and "chemically," before he managed to get his company started. A less determined man might have given up after the second or third attempt; Herbert Dow went on to the seventh or eighth—and succeeded.

The end result was that he, perhaps as much as any man, helped give America a chemical industry independent of foreign nations. He pioneered the mass production of a great many chemicals useful to industry and to everyday life, thus cutting their cost to a fraction of what it had been. His various electrolytic cells helped open up the whole field of electro-chemistry. More than any man, he helped this country develop its own supply of magnesium. He was the first in America commercially to synthesize indigo, "King of the Dyes." He developed, in the face of science's warnings that it couldn't be done, methods of manufacturing phenol that revolutionized a whole sector of American industry, and opened the way for dozens of now familiar products. He developed methods of manufacturing iodine that broke the foreign monopoly of this product and tremendously reduced its cost. He pointed the way to the successful "mining" of the world's greatest reservoir of valuable chemicals—the ocean.

How could a man, starting with little except ideas and determination as capital, accomplish so much? The men who worked with him attribute a great deal of his success to his personal character. Indeed, The Dow Chemical Company has sometimes been called "a projection of Herbert Dow's personality"—a description which the company proudly accepts.

In any case, Herbert Dow's character was firmly laid down in his boyhood and youth, and grew to maturity during his years of early struggle. It is therefore useful to begin his story by examining briefly how it all started.

PREPARATION FOR
A MISSION

Herbert dow's ancestors were all new englanders. the original dow, Henry, came from England in 1637 to settle in Massachusetts; he later moved to New Hampshire.

Joseph Dow, Herbert's father, seems to have been the first of the family to leave New England. Joseph Dow was a master mechanic, and appears to have combined in himself the skills nowadays divided among the inventor, the design engineer, and the expert machinist. He seems to have been the first American pioneer in the field of steam turbines; a turbine which he invented was for some time used by the United States Navy to power its torpedoes.

Starting soon after the American Civil War, industry began edging toward its present emphasis on mass production and constant improvement of processes and products. Industry also began fanning out from New England, which teemed with men of Yankee ingenuity like Joseph Dow. Such men were much in demand in this technically and geographically expanding picture. Joseph Dow was called away from New England twice: temporarily in 1865 and permanently in 1878.

The temporary call was to Belleville, Ontario, where Joseph Dow went to help operate a sewing machine factory. Herbert Dow was born at Belleville in 1866, and soon after that the family returned to Birmingham (now Derby) in Connecticut, where they were to live till Herbert was twelve.

Herbert's boyhood was happy, active, and bristling with some pretty precocious free enterprise. At age ten, for instance, he singlehandedly financed a visit to the Centennial Exposition, down in Philadelphia. He earned the money for this by an unusual technique for distributing handbills announcing the chronic "sales" at the town's drygoods store. What was unusual about the boy's technique was its break with tradition: he actually put one on each front porch, instead of distributing a few and contriving to lose the rest. For this new approach to handbill distributing he demanded —and got—a man's wages. He put this money in a little bank he himself made, and kept it there till there was enough to take him to the Exposition.

A more complex juvenile business venture of his stemmed from the negligent habits of ostriches. These birds, he read in *Youth's Companion*, laid plenty of eggs but seldom bothered to hatch them. Someone in Australia had worked out a sort of incubator to do this job for them. Incubators for eggs were then pretty much unknown, and the boy set about devising one that would hatch chicken eggs. The big problem, he soon found, was to work out a device that would automatically regulate the temperature. On his fortieth try, he contrived such a device, and made some incubators and sold them. One, in fact, went to a California egg rancher for $100.00.

Presently, however, he found orders for incubators declining. Purchasers had been buying his incubators for the same reason the Russians used to buy an occasional American automobile—to make copies and sell them. Instead of becoming indignant, Herbert dropped out of the incubator market for a while, and then came back in from a different direction. The really economical way to get a good incubator, he informed his public, was to buy his plans or blueprints and build your own. He sold such plans till he had filled his market for homemade incubators—whereupon he went on to something else.

In the course of his adult business life, Dow was often to repeat the above pattern. He would think of something that people would probably use if they had it, and then set about finding ways to make and sell it as economically as possible. If he ran into mechanical difficulties, as with the automatic heat regulator, he would hammer at them till he solved them or was satisfied they couldn't be solved. And when competition, fairly or unfairly, took advantage of what he had accomplished, he never let this upset him. Instead, he devised some way around or through the competitive situation. Meanwhile, he would be bearing in mind that the particular product might one day wear out its welcome, and he would be preparing to come to the market place with something else. Herbert Dow was a determined man, but his determination did not include trying to make people buy what they no longer needed, or what he could not make and sell more economically than his competitors.

In 1878, when Herbert was twelve years old, the family moved to Cleveland, Ohio. There his father became master mechanic at the Chisholm Steel Shovel Works. The family lived in a big house at the corner of Superior and

Case Avenues, kept a goat in the yard, and were consistent churchgoers. Herbert laid out a vegetable garden and sold produce to neighbors; he organized a church quartet, which he named The Pan Handle. The quartet gave special concerts whenever the minister's salary fell in arrears, which seems to have been fairly often.

Two factors in Herbert Dow's formative years cannot be overemphasized as influences on his way of thinking and on certain patterns of thought by which The Dow Chemical Company grew and still grows. One of these factors has already been hinted at: the boy's closeness to his father. These were the Victorian days, and it was not widely customary for fathers to associate with their children as if the children were people too. A father was expected to be a creature of vast dignity and if necessary wear a beard to prove it; it was a rare father indeed who actually let down the bars with his children and romped with them.[1] Joseph Dow seems not to have known of this required attitude, or to have ignored it if he did. In any case, he was forever discussing his turbine ideas with young Herbert as if the boy were a professional engineer; even at meals they were constantly passing rough sketches back and forth between them, in the manner of engineers to this day.

There seems to have been a great deal of discussion between the pair, too, about the pin factory in Derby where the father had worked for some time. The father's job there was to modernize the machinery which put the pins into papers for sale; the aim was to make the machines so efficient that a staff of girls would not have to be maintained to fill in the omissions by hand. This seems an odd problem for a small boy to interest himself in; the fact is that Herbert Dow was interested in such matters his whole life. Indeed, much of his industrial success was based on this very interest. He was not only what might be called an "inventive chemist"; he was also an industrialist very much preoccupied with the mechanical side of making chemicals in volume, accurately, and economically. Men who worked with him never have decided whether Herbert Dow should be thought of primarily as a chemist or an engineer. The answer probably is that he was both, and a third thing besides: a man curiously adept at combining the two.

---

[1] As late as the 1900's, many very fine people were shocked to hear of Teddy Roosevelt's floor-rollings with his children in the White House. This resembled the experience of a noted writer of the day who tried to run a humorous column in a Boston newspaper. He gave up, remarking that being funny in Boston was like making faces in church; it did no actual harm, but did offend lots of very nice people.

Corliss steam engine, considered a prodigy of size and power in Dow's boyhood. Hearing it was going to be on exhibition at the Philadelphia Centennial of 1876, the boy earned and saved money to go and see it. As a manufacturing chemist, Dow was extremely "power plant conscious." However much he might economize on building materials, he was constantly in search of bigger and more efficient machinery to make his continuous processes more productive. It was, of course, to be years before he could afford anything as big as this Corliss engine; today The Dow Chemical Company uses some of the world's biggest power units.

Turbine designed and built by Joseph H. Dow in the 1880's. It developed the then amazing speed of 25,000 to 30,000 revolutions a minute, and appears to have been the first American turbine. Herbert Dow got much of his insight into mechanics and power from close association with his father. The son once remarked that if his father had been as astute about patents as he was about inventing, he might have become a rich man. The sketch is Joseph Dow's indication of the principle involved.

The point of all this is that it was as a boy that Herbert Dow got his first glimpse of the budding techniques of mass production, and that his father did everything in his power to feed the boy's growing interest in it. The result was that when Herbert Dow came to set up as a manufacturing chemist, he already had some idea of what the score was. He knew in advance that the "manufacturing" was as important as the "chemistry"—that a piece of equipment, however inconspicuous, can be as important to the success of a new industrial chemical process as the chemical formula, however revolutionary, on which it is based. Thus it is that we will find him, throughout his career, dividing his efforts between devising new and better chemical formulas, and devising the machinery to make them work in the factory. His associates in later life often spoke of him as "a man of a million ideas." This would work out to a half-million each on chemistry and engineering, and may not be an exaggeration.[2]

Aside from his close and productive association with his father, perhaps the most important factor in Herbert Dow's early life was his matriculation at the Case School of Applied Science, in Cleveland. This institution was what its name indicated: a place where science was applied to the problems of industry. On the faculty were such men as Dr. John E. Stockwell, later famous as an astronomer, and Dr. Albert A. Michelson, who was to win the Nobel Prize for his work in physics. The atmosphere of the school was one of hammer-and-tongs investigation of the laws of nature, with the accent on making them work for the benefit of mankind. The most direct and practical place to do this was in the field of engineering; and that is where most of Herbert Dow's fellow students were enrolled.

With an independence characteristic of him, however, Herbert Dow enrolled in the field that as yet had little application to industry—chemistry. Why he did this, no one knows.[3] He had up to this time had no contact with chemists, nor shown any interest in chemistry. In this country, chemists and their science were still pretty completely confined to the laboratory, and it

[2] An uncle of Herbert's seems to have foreseen this, though in a mild way. He told the boy when he was still in grade school: "You have so many ideas that it would take six men to carry them out." Herbert replied: "I'll get the six men, but they won't be enough." At the time of his death in 1930, scores of chemists and engineers were working full blast at ideas he had directly or indirectly suggested.

[3] Miss Mary Dow, his sister, recalls that his original ambition was to be an architect. But to go to college he needed a scholarship; the only scholarship he received was to Case, and Case had no course in architecture. Years later, one of Herbert Dow's sons, Alden, became one of the nation's leading architects.

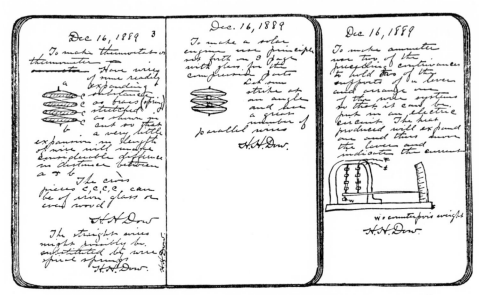

Dow ideas for a thermostat, a solar engine, and an ammeter. Actually, these represent three proposed uses of expansion and contraction due to heat. Electricity was just then coming into general use, and Dow was to be one of the pioneers in applying it to chemistry, both for electrolysis and for automatic controls. He and his associates sometimes worked months and even years to discover principles and methods now absorbed in a few minutes by undergraduates in technical schools.

is likely that Dow had never been in a chemical laboratory till he went to Case. In any event, he got into one at Case, and he spent the rest of his life translating laboratory possibilities into factory actualities. He was one of the first men in America to do this on a large and ever-expanding scale—and that was to be one of his major contributions to this country's chemical industry.

Incidentally, his connection with Case lasted through his lifetime. He and Case had the same inquiring and practical spirit: at Case you were not so much taught as encouraged to find out. It is not surprising that when he established his company and needed men to work on his multitudinous ideas, he turned often to Case. Two of his contemporaries there were to be especially close to him throughout his career: A. W. Smith and James T. Pardee. Smith was a year ahead of Dow; Pardee was in his class and, Dow always said, "the brightest fellow in it."

In his senior year at Case, Dow had to write a thesis. The chemistry of boiler fuels struck him as a good, practical subject, and he started to travel around Cleveland collecting boiler fuels to examine. One of these fuels was the natural gas often found in petroleum wells—and it was at such a well that the precise area of his future as an industrial chemist was decided.

Someone—an unidentified well driller—gave the young student a bottle of brine. It was on such brine, often encountered in oil-well drilling and considered a nuisance, that Herbert Dow later founded and developed The Dow Chemical Company.

Dow took the bottle of brine back to the Case laboratory and analyzed it. He managed to finish his thesis on boiler fuels, but the real interest of his life was now brine. Whenever possible, he traveled about Ohio and Michigan in day coaches, gathering samples of brine to analyze. His graduation from Case left him without a laboratory to analyze in. He solved this by engaging to do for a year what most of the few chemists of his day did for life: teach chemistry to others. This was at the Huron Street Hospital College, in Cleveland. They gave him what was for a youth the grandiloquent title of "Professor of Chemistry and Toxicology," a few dollars to live on— and a laboratory he could use in his spare time to analyze and experiment with brine.

Meanwhile, he was getting clear in his mind what others were doing about brine. It was not a clean-cut and well-organized picture. Under certain mid-continental areas, especially Ohio and Michigan, lay vast underground stores of "fossilized sea water" or brine, trapped usually in porous rock. This liquid contained, in various compounds and much diluted, ample supplies of five valuable chemical elements: bromine, chlorine, calcium, magnesium, and sodium. Here was, so to speak, a gold mine of natural resources. But the limited chemical industry of the day was interested in only two of its possible products: bromine and sodium chloride, or salt.

But even bromine and salt were of interest only sporadically and under particular circumstances. The chief of these circumstances was cheapness of local fuel. If there was plenty of cheap fuel around, it might be worth while to pump brine out of the ground into vats, and heat it till enough water had been evaporated to make it give up its salt. A common cheap fuel in those days was scrap wood from lumber mills, of which there were still a great many in Michigan in the last century: this accounts for the multitude of "salt and lumber companies" with which the state then abounded. After cheapness of fuel, the controlling factor was whether the salt so obtained was pure enough to be usable and therefore salable: sometimes it was and sometimes it wasn't. Another factor, of course, was whether there was enough demand for salt at the particular time and place to make it worth recovering.

Much the same factors governed the production of bromine, which remained in the "bittern" or mother liquor after the salt had crystallized out. If there was a demand for bromine, and fuel was cheap, it was worth while to recover it. This was done usually by adding suitable chemicals to the bittern to release the bromine, and heating the mixture till the bromine came off as a gas, mixed with steam. There were numerous small companies that undertook to do this, but few of them on a steady basis. When bromine was wanted by the pharmaceutical houses, chiefly for patent medicines, the little companies sprang into operation; when there was no market, the companies shut down. Even when they did operate, it was on a "batch basis."

There were a number of things about this whole situation which struck the young professor as needlessly uneconomical, and which he therefore looked on as challenges. For one thing, if the salt in the brine was often no good for sale, it seemed to him almost an imposition that this salt had to be removed before the brine would give up its small content of bromine. He therefore required himself to find a way to obtain the bromine without the expense and nuisance of first removing the salt.

Another thing that annoyed him was the direct dependence on cheap local fuel, especially in such accidental and temporary forms as local lumber-mill waste. Lumbering operations in those days were savagely wasteful, but young Dow saw that even this determined creation of debris could not go on indefinitely in any one location. When the trees were all cut down and the wreckage all burned, fuel might no longer be local or cheap. He therefore wanted a way to get the two or three pounds of bromine out of a ton of brine without expending heat to evaporate most of the ton.

Finally, he did not like the business of working in start-and-stop batches. There must be some way, he felt sure, to produce so much bromine an hour, twenty-four hours a day, day in and day out. Such an operation, especially if automatically controlled, would produce more bromine more economically and so would make for more attractive selling prices.

Such, then, were the requirements the young professor set himself to meet: no salt-making, no heating, no starting-and-stopping. The curious thing is not that he so correctly spotted these as the basic problems of the bromine industry, but that he got so soon onto the roadway toward the right answers to them.

As we shall presently see, the young professor would in a few years successfully revolutionize the whole American bromine industry, and earn his company a leadership in the field which it holds to this day. Much of his eventual success was due to a combination of two processes: electrolysis and "blowing out." The function of the electrolysis was to "free" the bromine

On Hand 31.98
Fare to Toledo 3 25
Peaches 05
Car fare 05
Hotel 1 00
Shave & Shine 20
Watch key 15
Peaches 05
Car fare 05
Hydrometer 75
Fare to Perrysburgh 2 0
Hotel 70
Fare to Findlay 1 30

31.98
7.10
24.88 On hand 7 80

Especially as a young man, Herbert Dow was forever filling notebooks with ideas, inventions and chemical processes. In the same notebooks he often put down his daily disbursements. Here is the financial background of a brine-investigating trip into Western Ohio. Note such bargains as hotel $.70 (including meals) and shave & shine $.20.

into the solution. Herbert Dow did not "discover," in his hospital laboratory or anywhere else, that the bromine can be freed by electrolysis. That had been known for some time. It is probable that he never even considered electrolysis at first. In any event, that development did not come till several years later, and then his contribution was to show that it could be done, more and more efficiently and productively, on a factory scale.

Actually, the big achievement of these hospital days was his blowing-out process. It seems to have taken almost its permanent form right there in his spare-time laboratory; he was to use it successfully in his very first plant; it is today, almost unchanged after over a half century, one of the unique and key processes used in Dow plants. Briefly, here is how it works:

Bromine is a reddish liquid which tends to vaporize even at ordinary room temperature. When set free in some such solution as brine, it begins gradually to vaporize and come off the solution. Heat makes it come off faster, but Dow was avoiding heat. He therefore hit upon the notion of passing a steady flow of air through the brine in which the bromine was freed, thus stimulating the exit of the bromine. To give this blown air more efficient access to the freed bromine, he was to try various ways of spreading the solution thin. In his first little factory, for instance, he had the air blow through sheets of burlap kept wet with the solution. Later he replaced burlap with wood laths. But that is a detail; the point is that he had already, in his early twenties, worked out a process which was to help change a whole industry.

By the spring of 1889, the young professor was convinced he was, at age twenty-three, ready to make bromine from brine on a profitable commercial basis. It was to take him about seven years really to prove this. Meanwhile, he would have to face and digest some pretty stern lessons. These lessons, as we are now going to see, involved certain grim realities of finance, of chemistry—and of human nature.

3

ADVENTURE IN CANTON: DOW AND BROMINE

HERBERT DOW'S FIRST ATTEMPT TO PRODUCE BROMINE ON A COMMERCIAL BASIS took place near Canton, Ohio. The vehicle of this attempt was something ambitiously christened the Canton Chemical Company.

If ever there was a "shoestring company," this was it. Not much is known of its organizational structure, except that it was a partnership consisting of Dow and Joseph P. Smith, a Cleveland egg merchant. Soon there were two additional partners—Jacob Miller and J. A. Linville, of the Buckeye Mower & Reaper Company, of Canton. The general arrangement seems to have been that his partners put up the money and Dow did the work. The difficulty here was that the partners were willing to put up only a few hundred dollars apiece. Dow's cash on hand at one point totaled $2.06; he spent the Fourth of July in Cleveland borrowing $50.00 to keep going.

Under these financial circumstances, this first "plant" of Dow's was hardly equipped to do much of a job. Such equipment as was not secondhand was third-hand or even fourth-hand, and spent a large part of its time breaking down. The real museum piece of the setup seems to have been the pump that Dow bought to draw brine from the well. It was so old that spare parts for it no longer existed. Even if they had existed, they would have been of small aid and comfort to Dow's Canton Chemical Company: for shippers demanded cash on delivery, and there was seldom cash. An added feature of Dow's pump troubles was that the well was three thousand feet deep, which was about all a pump in superb health could handle in those days.[1]

How much bromine the Canton Chemical Company actually produced is not known. One of Herbert Dow's diaries reports, with evident relish, that four gallons of ferric bromide were made on September 29, but production

---

[1] And twice the depth that Dow attempted again to handle till many years later. Dow's faith in himself and his ideas was often to ambush him with handicaps a less self-confident man would have sidestepped.

```
·····················
: THE DOW AIR BATTERY COMPANY,
:    735 SOCIETY FOR SAVINGS BUILDING,        CLEVELAND, OHIO.
:              TESTS, VOLTS,              AMPERES
:   This is a Dry Battery and is ready for immediate use, without further preparation.  It needs
: no attention whatever, and no renewal of parts until fully exhausted.  It must not be opened or its
: operation will be destroyed, and this side should be kept up to secure greatest durability.
:       THE ABOVE TEST IS GUARANTEED.                    Patents Pending )
·····················
```

An 1891 side venture of Herbert Dow's. Little came of it at the time. But in 1918 the National Carbon Company bought the method to help itself around a shortage of raw materials for dry batteries it was making.

fell off to a couple of gallons the next day. The only known sale occurred on November 4, when 23 carboys were sold for $69.93. By the end of December, the Canton Chemical Company seems to have ceased whatever operations there were; on April 25, 1890, well before its first birthday, the partnership was formally dissolved.

So Dow, now aged twenty-four, went back to Cleveland to try to raise funds to set up another company to try again.

HOWEVER MUCH OF A FIASCO the defunct venture may have seemed to his partners, it appears not to have struck Herbert Dow in that light at all. It's a good thing it didn't, for its chief elements were to keep reappearing in his ventures for the next several years. One of these elements was chronic shortness of money, either for proper equipment or for working capital. This meant that there was constant pressure to do original and expert work with ramshackle or jury-rigged equipment, a pressure Dow was to know only too well for the next six or eight years.

This shortness of money introduced the young man to another facet of industrial life with which he was to become only too familiar for a while—that when the manger is empty, the horses tend to bite one another. Dow's Canton partners wanted a big and quick return on their few hundred dollars; he needed more money to get them any return at all. This difference in financial outlook occasioned some pretty brisk uproars; Dow was to spend the next seven years in the thick of this sort of thing. So far as is known, the bites he sustained in these uproars never embittered him, as they might have a less practical man. On the positive side, they taught him a lifelong respect for the industrial dollar, whether his company was earning it or paying it out. He insisted to the end of his days on both receiving and giving full value; he would not cut corners himself, or knowingly let anyone cut corners on him.

There were lessons other than financial ones that young Dow learned all too clearly at Canton. One concerned the great difference in the behavior of chemicals in the laboratory and out in the factory. Chemicals in some ways resemble small boys: in limited quantity and "controlled" surroundings, they can behave like angels. In volume, however, and with more freedom to display their true nature, both small boys and chemicals can become imps and even devils. At Canton, Dow had a chance to handle brine and bromine on only a relatively modest factory scale. Even so, he became very aware of their corrosive nature. Later, at Midland, when he began to handle them in quantity, he learned at first hand of their skill at destroying what were to him almost priceless copper wiring and generator parts.

Perhaps the most important fact about Dow's Canton venture was that he tried his blowing-out process, and it worked. Cold brine in which the bromine had been freed by chemicals was allowed to drip like a slow rain into a large box filled with taut strips of burlap. A steady draft of air from the floor circulated upwards through the wet burlap, carrying the bromine off with it in the form of a reddish-brown gas. The bromine-laden air next passed through a tangle of wet iron-wire scrap. The water, bromine, and iron formed a solution of ferric bromide, which dripped down and was caught in carboys and sold. At least we know that Dow sold 23 carboys of it, at $3.04 a carboy. This was hardly enough to keep the Canton Chemical Company in business. But it did prove, to Dow's satisfaction, that his blowing-out process would help him get bromine without using heat. The ironical thing is that even at Canton, this first "cold" method of Dow's proved *theoretically* more economical than the usual "hot" process he was avoiding. There were three very good reasons why it did not prove to be so in fact.

One was that the process still contained crudities that would have to be worked out. Another was that he had no money to set the process up in a respectable manner. Most important of all, perhaps, was the fact that his well pump wasn't in working mood often enough to keep the process going with any steadiness.

In the next several years, the young man was to have many failures for one or more of the above reasons. And always, rather than see these reasons as excuses for not trying again, he saw them as temporary obstacles to be removed. It was in that constructive frame of mind that he left Canton to set out again to make and sell bromine more economically than anyone else.

4

DOW COMES TO MIDLAND

PERHAPS IT SHOULD HAVE BEEN A THOROUGHLY HUMILIATED YOUNG MAN WHO shut down the little wellside plant at Canton and went back to Cleveland. The fact is, however, that it was a very confident young man who walked into the office of the National Carbon Company in Cleveland early in 1890 and asked to see Mr. J. H. Osborn, one of the executives. Mr. Osborn was an old friend of the Dow family, but the young man was not coming to him for sympathy. He was coming for money to start another bromine company, and he got it—a few thousand dollars to be paid in installments. The two men formed a partnership, to which Dow's contribution seems to have been his belief in himself, his faith in his proposed cold-brine process, and the hard lessons administered to him at Canton.

These somewhat intangible assets, together with Mr. Osborn's few thousand dollars, Herbert Dow proposed to put to work at Midland, a small town in Michigan. Dow had passed through Midland a couple of years before, collecting brine samples to analyze. To anyone but him, the place must have looked like a town with its future firmly behind it. There were fourteen saloons, a brief business street, a few wooden sidewalks, no street lights, two covered bridges, and the homes, some of them pretty nondescript, of two thousand townsfolk. What interested Herbert Dow, however, was the scattering of crude wooden towers that dotted the immediate countryside. These were, he knew, the derricks of salt wells. Years later he wrote how they got there and why they attracted him to Midland, with which he was to be identified for the rest of his life:

In those days Midland County was especially favored because of the size and number of its white pine trees, and the fact that its streams [1] made it possible to float the logs to suitable points where sawmills converted them into lumber. These sawmills were first built at Saginaw and Bay City, and later at Midland. Saginaw

[1] The Tittabawassee River flows past the Dow plant.

18

lumbermen had discovered that salt brine existed in the earth under their mills, and the industry of pumping this brine and evaporating it with heat obtained from the waste lumber from the sawmills grew very rapidly. Midland lumbermen soon followed the example of their Saginaw competitors and drilled wells in Midland to pump brine. It was a gala day in Midland when the first well began operating, though nobody dreamed at that time of it containing any substance of value other than common salt, and it was not until some years later that Al Dickey's brother, who had been making bromine on the Ohio River, visited Midland and upon testing the brine found that it contained a large amount of bromine.

He erected a plant for its recovery, and the business grew rapidly; until at the time of my visit in 1888, when I collected samples of the brine, Midland had become the largest single producer of bromine in the world. By the old process of extracting bromine, which had been in use since bromine first became a commercial commodity in 1825, it was necessary to make salt in conjunction with bromine. At the time of my arrival in Midland in 1890 the salt industry of this section had become very much overdone, so that even the combined manufacture of salt and bromine was proving unprofitable. It was therefore an opportune time for the appearance of my process, which removed the bromine without evaporating the brine.

Although Mr. Osborn seems to have been willing enough to back Dow, the partnership agreement was not signed till August 12, 1890. The organization was given the name Midland Chemical Company. In the next several years, the structure of the Midland Chemical Company was to undergo various changes. These changes were usually inspired by Herbert Dow in the interests of getting more capital to carry out his ideas. Dow was always the company's moving spirit, though on one occasion he was almost moved out for "risking" the organization's future by getting interested in the chlorine content of brine, along with its very much smaller bromine content. It was not till 1895, five years after his arrival in Midland, that Herbert Dow formed the Dow Process Company to give his ideas about chlorine freer rein, and the present Dow Chemical Company, which took over the Dow Process Company and the Midland Chemical Company, was not formed till 1897.

In short, it was not until several years after his arrival in Midland that Herbert Dow was at last able to set up and operate a company as he felt it should be set up and operated; though meanwhile he was to carry, without corresponding power, the responsibility of making the undertaking work. He was to find those years difficult, strenuous and generally lean. Some idea of their leanness may be gained from these entries in one of his notebooks for the year 1890:

Tues., Aug. 12: Received of Mr. Osborn $100 in cash and $275 draft.
Wed., Aug. 13: Started for Midland.
Thurs., Aug. 14: Arrived in Midland.
Sat., Aug. 16: Made deposit of $275 in bank. Began boarding at Antler House this noon.
Mon., Aug. 18: Teamster ½ day. Frank Evans ¼ day. Mr. Aldrich 8 hours. Mr. Hitchcock, Jr., ½ day. Mr. Dent 3 hours. Cleaned tank and did part of grading and cleaning up.
Tues., Aug. 19: Tried steam to engine but pipe was burst.
Thurs., Aug. 21: $36.90 on hand in the morning before going to Saginaw.
Thurs., Sept. 10: (Cleveland) Paid Judge Jones $3.00 consultation fee.
Mon., Sept. 15: Started for Washington.
Tues., Sept. 16: Went to Smithsonian Institute. Saw still made by John Cliff, Eng.
Thurs., Sept. 18: Arrived in Cleveland.
Sun., Sept. 21: Got sick. Called Dr. Jones.
Tues., Sept. 30: Arrived in Midland. Began to room at Mrs. Olmstead's.
Sun., Oct. 6: Took class of boys at Sunday School.

What problem Herbert Dow had gone to the Smithsonian to solve is not known. In any event, he came back to Midland ready, he thought, to combine his ideas of an electrolytic cell, blowing-out, and continuous production into a plant that could make bromine better, faster, and cheaper than anyone else. The young man was now in for a series of jolts that were to make his Canton experiences seem like a succession of pats on the back.

His first problem, of course, was shortness of money. He had nowhere near enough to set up a plant, but that is what he contrived somehow to do. At the western end of Midland's brief main street stood the Evans Flour Mill. Nearby stood an old barn; between them a disused well reached down to the underground brine. Dow made a deal for the use of the well and of the barn. He wanted to try his electrolytic scheme, but there was no electricity to be bought. He therefore acquired a 15-volt generator to make his own electricity, and set it up in the barn. To turn this generator, he bought permission to run a homemade rope drive from the mill's steam engine into the barn.[2]

He now had power and brine: all he needed was to put the power to work on the brine. In his hospital days and at Canton, he had made repeated

[2] We get a pretty clear indication of what a tiny infant electrolytic chemistry then was from this paragraph of a letter Dow wrote a quarter century later: "The electrolytic manufacture of bromine was started in Midland in the summer of 1890. In this work it was intended to use four electrolytic cells in series and with this

notebook sketches of the cell in which he intended to do this. Now he built such a cell—the first crude ancestor of the famous Dow electrolytic cells so important to the modern chemical industry. The current, in passing through the brine, was expected to free the bromine, which would then be blown out and made into ferric bromide, as at Canton.

And that is precisely what happened, as we know from these laconic entries in one of Dow's notebooks:

Dec. 8, 1890: Teaming 35 cents. Got 2 barrels of iron from pail factory; they weigh about 175 pounds each.
Tues., Dec. 9: Tried the dynamo.
Wed., Dec. 10: On hand $1.80. Julius Burow and I are connecting carbons in circuit.[3]
Jan. 2, 1891: Started pump at 7 A.M. On hand $2.26.
Jan. 4, 1891: Bromide of iron started running for first time this morning. Ran power 24 hours.

What these brief entries were reporting was his first factory production of bromine by means of electrolysis. So far as is known, and certainly so far as Dow knew, no one else had ever achieved this. Thus the first of the many dreams he was to have in his career had come true, though in small and crude form.

But there was, he soon found, room for only limited jubilation. His operation was on too small a scale to produce enough bromine to pay its own way, much less show a profit. In short, he needed more money.

This need inevitably took him to Cleveland and his friend, Mr. Osborn. Together they asked a Cleveland bank to lend $20 a day for operating expenses. The bank, after some hesitation, agreed—but apparently frightened Dow off by requiring control of the little company till it had paid back the

end in view, a 15 volt generator was purchased, although great difficulty was experienced in securing a machine of this abnormally high voltage, as all the electric plating people said that experience with voltage higher than 5 or 6 had been uniformly unsatisfactory. We finally secured a machine, but were only able to operate it with three cells in series, because the machine itself had a hard time to maintain more than 12 or 13 volts after it had warmed up."

[3] Burow was one of Dow's workmen. Dow's notebooks teem with their names, which is not surprising: for years he spent more time working along with them than he spent in the office or even the laboratory. In fact, he was a familiar figure out in the factory up to the time of his death, long after he had become internationally famous. This was no pose for him; his lifework was making his chemical ideas work out on a factory scale, and he wanted to see at first hand how things were coming.

loan. Instead, Dow and Osborn persuaded two Clevelanders, W. L. Hulburt and B. H. Howe, to put up a little money in return for admission to the partnership. Dow went back to Midland with this new money. But within a few months he was writing to Mr. Howe: "I have not paid Dickey for last acid and am nearly out of money."

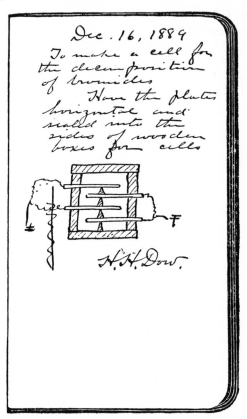

Earliest known ancestor, on paper at least, of the long line of Dow electrolytic cells. The drawing was made at the time of the Canton venture, when Dow was twenty-three. A few years later, he became the first man to produce bromine commercially by electrolysis.

The reference to acid indicates Dow had dropped electrolysis for the moment and was using the better-known method of freeing the bromine by adding chemicals. It is possible that the new partners insisted upon his returning to this more accepted method. But he never gave up, even for the moment, his cherished blowing-out process.

Meanwhile, Dow found himself writing more and more pleas for money.

There were brief respites from financial pressure, as when he wrote to Howe in April of 1891:

Your letter containing N. Y. draft for seventy-five dollars just received. I think that will give us enough funds to last for quite a while.

But several weeks later he was writing of one of his workmen:

Albert was going to leave us, but I got him to stay by agreeing to pay for his overalls.

Soon it was clear even to young Dow that he would either have to find more backing or give up for good. It was not in his nature to give up, and so he went back to Cleveland again in search of more capital.

This time he had better luck. With Mr. Osborn's help, he was able to persuade a group of men to form a corporation to replace the capital-hungry partnership. This corporation was to have 10,000 shares of stock at $10 par value—for a mouth-watering total of $100,000. Incorporators were Mr. Osborn; B. E. Helman, a Cleveland merchant; W. B. Remington, a mill owner; W. W. Cooper, a St. Joseph, Mich., businessman; Thomas Percy, a Michigan well driller who had little to put up but his skill; and Herbert Dow, who was pretty much in the same boat. They met at Midland on August 17, 1892, to incorporate as the Midland Chemical Company and elect the following officers: president, W. B. Remington; first vice-president, J. H. Osborn; second vice-president, Thomas Percy; secretary, W. W. Cooper; and treasurer, B. E. Helman. Dow was to build and run the plant as general manager.

It must have been a great day for the young man when the papers were signed and he had at least a promised $100,000 behind him. He had planned to build his new and larger plant for about $27,500, and he hoped that at least that much would be subscribed in cash. Only about $10,000 came in, however; and for a while it appeared Dow was back in the old familiar pattern—with not enough money to set up operations on a scale that would pay.

That load was partially removed from his mind when a Cleveland bank granted the Midland Chemical Company a credit of $10,000. He was now ready to try again, though under a handicap which he himself seems not to have suspected at the time. This one involved a battle of human wills, and it was to present the unusual spectacle of Herbert Dow coming off second best.

SUCCESS—AND DISILLUSION

HERBERT DOW NOW HAD, FOR THE FIRST TIME, ENOUGH MONEY TO SET UP A plant of commercial proportions. His first step was to leave his barn quarters beside the flour mill, and move onto a corner of what is now The Dow Chemical Company's site, on the other end of town. There he had Thomas Percy, second vice-president and well driller, put down two brine wells. Then he set about building the plant in which the brine from these wells was to be stripped of its bromine.

Specifications for the plant came from Dow's notebooks, and economy was at all times the keynote. Nothing that could be made of wood was made of anything else. Wood was cheap around Midland; even so, Dow himself shopped endlessly among the lumber mills, looking for bargains that would suit his purpose. Railroad freight rates were then pretty flexible, and shippers were expected to argue for reductions; when Dow found his bargains in lumber at some distance from the plant, he made deals to have it hauled to him cheaply, in return for the business he hoped soon to provide in the hauling away of bromine. Even nails were economized on. Dow heard of a study done at a state college on the most economical spacing of nails in roofs and walls. He wrote for the study, and spaced his nails accordingly.

It is easy to smile at the young man's detailed and relentless economy. To an extent, Herbert Dow had it forced on him; but it was part of his whole industrial philosophy even then. He was to spend his life making dexterous use of inexpensive materials, with the aim of producing useful things economically and reflecting this economy in his prices. It would be hard to think, for instance, of a more economical raw material than the brine under Midland. Most people considered it entirely worthless, or at best useful for its few pounds of bromine per ton. Yet from this same "worthless" brine Dow and his associates were to develop, within a very few years, some hundred and fifty useful products.

Wood in Midland. A typical shingle mill of Dow's early days in Midland. Waste wood was used to boil down brine from underground, producing salt and bromine. By the time of Dow's arrival in Midland, the wood was beginning to run out and the bromine and salt business to vanish. Dow and his electrolytic process were eventually to make Midland the bromine center of the United States.

Scene of Herbert Dow's first successful electrolysis of brine to produce bromine commercially. To the right is the Evans Flour Mill described in the text. The tower houses the brine well. Dow worked on his brine in the shed to the left. The mill stood on Midland's Main Street, near the site of the present water tower.

Midland Chemical Company in 1894. This was the first bromine plant built just as Dow wanted it, and here he made the electrolytic manufacture of bromine from brine a commercial success for the first time. The plant was built of lumber obtained at bargain rates by Dow, but the generator was the largest and most powerful he could find.

Probably most of the working force of the Midland Chemical Company sometime in 1894.

The new plant was set up, of course, around electrolysis and blowing-out. The blowing-out process was arranged much as at Canton and as at the Evans Mill venture. Dow did make, though, an important change in his electrolytic process. Each of the large troughlike cells was partitioned into a series of smaller cells. Carbon electrodes pierced the board partitions carrying the current from the brine in one cell into the brine in the next. This new kind of cell, set up in series, required a more powerful generator than the 15-volt unit he had been using.

Dow accordingly sent to Cleveland for a 50-kilowatt generator. Such a unit is of course commonplace nowadays. But this was in 1892; and here, as Dow later wrote, is what happened:

We built a larger plant and decided to put many cells in series and go up to 100 volts. We estimated that 50 KW would be required for this work and we sent to the Cleveland office of the General Electric Company (just formed from the old Thompson-Huston-Edison Companies) and asked them to bid on a 100 volt 50 KW generator. We found that their Cleveland agent had no conception of the meaning of the word "kilowatt" and wanted us to specify our requirements in number of lights instead of kilowatts. Another firm wanted to furnish it in three units, because they said that while it was entirely practicable to run 50 KW for lighting load in the evening, for continuous services sizes as large as 50 KW had not proved satisfactory. We finally got a National machine from Eau Claire, Wisconsin, and it was the largest machine they had ever made.

That was, by the way, a situation Dow encountered a great many times in his career. In his eagerness to push the boundaries of industrial chemistry forward, he was often far in advance of the capacities of other industries whose help he required.

Incidentally, it may at first glance seem inconsistent that Dow would count nails in bargain-priced lumber, and then scour the countryside for the best electrical equipment obtainable. Actually, both policies were a form of economy: they were his way of making each of his plant dollars contribute its utmost in finished product. Besides, he required his equipment to work twenty-four hours a day, which was a daring concept in the 1890's. Units like generators were accustomed to stand side by side and "spell" each other—a system which did not appeal to Dow's economical mind. At the same time, he realized his equipment *had to* be the best to meet his requirements of it; and from here on we will find him sparing no legitimate expense to obtain the best.

Another innovation at the new plant was the kind of bromide made.

Because of its volatility, it was usual to "fix" bromine into some such compound as ferric bromide, sodium bromide, or potassium bromide for ease in handling and shipping. Up to now, Dow had been making ferric (that is, iron) bromide—probably for the simple reason it was the easiest for him to make. Now he undertook to make potassium bromide, which was where the chief market was anyway.

This decision to make potassium bromide, plus difficulty with his new electrolytic process, was for a while to cause him considerable trouble: his product was too impure for ready sale. One of these impurities was chlorine, to whose presence in the product the drug houses violently objected. The chlorine got in because Dow was at first unable to regulate his electrolytic method properly. Too weak a current passing through the brine failed to liberate all the bromine, and thus was uneconomical. Too strong a current liberated the bromine, but also some chlorine, which got into the final product. It took the young man many long days and nights of study and watchfulness to get the current just right.

With the chlorine problem solved, he still had the other impurities to deal with. Most of these entered the product via the homemade potash he was using as a source of potassium. Most of the neighboring lumber mills had what they called "asheries," in which they reduced wood to ashes for sale to people like Dow. But wood ashes contain, besides potassium, an assortment of chemical odds and ends. Some of these disappeared during the making of potassium bromide, but a great many remained to turn up in the finished product. The answer to this was finally found. It was discovered that heating the potassium bromide to a molten mass oxidized or burned away most of the impurities. This step was added to the process, and Dow's product became a great deal more pure.

But it still wasn't quite up to *United States Pharmacopoeia* standards, and buyers knew how to take advantage of this whether they needed a product of that purity or not. Years later, Dow described one of his early experiences in this matter. His account is enlightening in several ways. It indicates the harsh and cynical tactics he was up against in his efforts to break into the market. And it shows how all phases of the work of the new company fell on him: in the midst of financial and technical problems, he had to travel around peddling his product by the barrel. Here is his account of his first sale:

When we got our first barrel of potassium bromide I attempted to sell it. I first went to a school friend in Cleveland, who was in the wholesale drug business. He did not use bulk bromides, but he took me to a man just starting in the brokerage business, to whom I stated that the price of potassium bromide was 35 cents a pound, but we were willing to sell it to him for 25 cents, and we were about to close a deal, when he said: "By the way, these bromides are strictly U.S.P., aren't they?" I said: "No, they are not strictly U.S.P., but are equal to the best on the market." He immediately replied that he could not use them, so I left him and went to an old reliable chemical house in another city. I explained that our goods were strictly U.S.P. in all respects but one, and in that one were fully equal to any brand on the market. They said they bought their goods from firms of high reputation, and that they did not dare buy from a little one-horse concern in Michigan—that it would affect their reputation if they did. However, they said they had a little business where purity was not so important and they might buy a little if the price was right, and they finally offered me 17 cents a pound—just one-half of the market price. I accepted an order for two barrels and went back to Midland. We opened up the barrels of bromides to see if they looked exactly right. Here and there we found specks, and they were not in as good form as they should be, and we spent most of the next two days picking over the two barrels of potassium bromide crystals to remove every speck or imperfect crystal.[1]

We then shipped the two barrels and waited for a remittance. When a letter eventually arrived it stated that they had examined the bromides and found that they were not strictly U.S.P. and asked what concession in price we would be willing to make. That letter sent my heart down into my boots. We needed the money very much. We had closed the deal, as we supposed—at one-half the market price. What further concession should we now make? Fortunately for the future success of the organization there happened to be a business man in our office who volunteered to answer the letter. In substance our reply was as follows: "We are in receipt of your letter of recent date. If the goods are not satisfactory, please return them."

I was so scared that the goods would be returned that after signing the letter I was afraid to put it in the post office, but finally did, and the next letter from the firm contained a check in full settlement.

That first precarious sale to Rosengarten & Sons, of Philadelphia, was made in 1893, and proved a harbinger of better financial days to come. In 1894, the little Midland Chemical Company seems to have sold all the potassium bromide it could make, and showed a profit of $11,781.78. The young man had proved for the first time that he could make money for his stockholders.

This was Herbert Dow's first financial success. There was every indication that his success would hold up—that is, continue to earn handsomely

[1] In which picking-over he was assisted by his young wife, the former Miss Grace A. Ball, a Midland girl. Like the Dows, the Balls were of early New England ancestry.

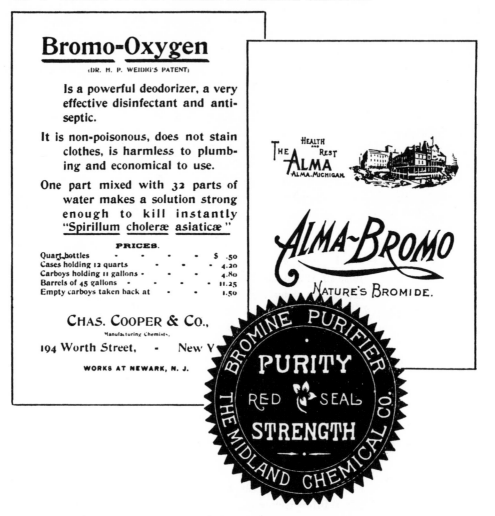

Bromo-Oxygen

(DR. H. P. WEIDIG'S PATENT)

Is a powerful deodorizer, a very effective disinfectant and antiseptic.

It is non-poisonous, does not stain clothes, is harmless to plumbing and economical to use.

One part mixed with 32 parts of water makes a solution strong enough to kill instantly "Spirillum choleræ asiaticæ"

PRICES.

Quart bottles	-	-	-	-	$ .50
Cases holding 12 quarts		-	-	-	4.20
Carboys holding 11 gallons -		-	-		4.80
Barrels of 45 gallons	-	-	-	-	11.25
Empty carboys taken back at		-	-		1.50

CHAS. COOPER & CO.,

Manufacturing Chemists,

194 Worth Street, - New Y...

WORKS AT NEWARK, N. J.

THE ALMA
HEALTH and REST
ALMA, MICHIGAN

ALMA-BROMO

NATURE'S BROMIDE.

BROMINE PURIFIER
PURITY
RED SEAL
STRENGTH
THE MIDLAND CHEMICAL CO.

Typical promotional material for patented bromine solutions of the 1890's. Once, when sales were off, Herbert Dow visited practically every drugstore in Detroit and Chicago in the interests of his Red Seal Bromine Purifier. Bromine always sold well during cholera scares, of which there were a great many in those days.

each year on the original investment. By the routine financial thinking of the time, to which his stockholders subscribed heartily, this should have made the young man very happy.

And it did—with one reservation. He wanted to expand. And he wanted to expand by the same method by which he was to go on expanding to the day of his death, and by which his company and the chemical industry are still expanding. *He wanted to find additional products to make and sell.*

Even before he made the bromine business successful, he had already hit upon the first of these additional products. This product was chloride of lime, familiarly known as "bleach."

There were a number of very practical reasons why Herbert Dow wanted to make bleach in addition to potassium bromide. For one thing, there was a growing demand for it. The textile industry, and especially the cotton mills, had always used some; now a new industry was coming up that wanted bleach, too. The linotype and rotary printing press had recently been invented; it had been discovered that very good paper could be made of wood pulp. This pulp needed, however, to be bleached, and Dow saw a growing market he was sure he could get into.

Another reason Dow wanted to make bleach was that its basis is chlorine —and the brine from which he was extracting bromine was far more rich in chlorine. This chlorine was being deliberately thrown away in the sewage that ran from the bromine plant. It was the most natural thing in the world for Dow to want to obtain this chlorine and use it.

Finally, he knew that chlorine had many more possible uses than bromine. Once he was producing chlorine, he could use it for bleach *and still additional products.*

Dow presented these views to his "home office" in Cleveland, where they were received without enthusiasm. It is not hard to understand why. For a long time, it had been touch and go whether Dow's bromine process would make any money. Now it was providing dividends of 2 or 3 per cent per month. The depression that started in 1893 was still on, and that 2 or 3 per cent a month was important money. Why gamble any of it on another venture that might or might not work, and in any case might take years in getting onto a dividend-paying basis?

It should be remembered, too, that research and new-product development did not have the same standing with businessmen of those days as it now enjoys. Those were pretty much the days of the "quick kill"—you made what you could on a going product, whacked up the profits, and concentrated on making more of the same product the next year. Only if your product "died on you" were you likely to look for a new one. Herbert Dow could never accept that short view; nor could he ever feel comfortable throwing away a natural resource like the chlorine in the waste brine from his plant. In this attitude, too, he was ahead of his time, when the tendency was to exploit wastefully every natural resource from the trees in the forest to the seals in the ocean.

In any case, the directors in Cleveland were not friendly to Dow's notion of expansion into chlorine and bleach. As if to emphasize their negative attitude, they demoted him from his post of general manager. Nevertheless, they did give him grudging permission to erect a small shed and some cells to work on the electrolysis of chlorine from brine. Here is Herbert Dow's own account of what happened:

When the bromide plant began to operate successfully and profitably, it was only natural that I should apply the methods that had already been perfected for the manufacture of bromine to the extraction of the similar substance, chlorine, as compounds made from chlorine had an enormously greater field than those made from bromine. We therefore built an electrolytic plant for making electrolytic chlorine in the summer of 1895. When finally completed the current was turned on in the forenoon and at twelve o'clock when everybody was out of the building, about an hour after the current had first been turned on, it blew up with a tremendous explosion, entirely destroying the apparatus in the building, and even injuring the adjoining building, but fortunately no person was hurt. A meeting of the Board of Directors was called and it was decided that they did not care to do any more expanding.

In short, it was decided to nip in the bud, once and for all, the young man's whole concept of what a chemical company owed itself, its stockholders, and its public: growth in usefulness. Nor did the directors stop there. They voted that Herbert Dow was to patent his chlorine process in the name of the Midland Chemical Company, and offer it for sale to some outside company—the proceeds of the sale to go to the credit of the Midland Chemical Company. The group already owned his bromine process; the patents on it were about all he had been able to put up for his small holdings of stock. He had also agreed to patent in the group's name any other brine developments he made: he had no recourse.

Thus, at age twenty-nine, Herbert Dow found himself in the bleak position that many a pioneer and inventor has found himself in before and since. He had accomplished just enough to suit the purposes of his backers, and what he had accomplished belonged legally to them. In return, he was on the pay roll at a nominal salary, owned a nominal portion of stock, and had a correspondingly nominal voice in the use to be made of his achievements.

That sort of deal has been the end of many an earnest pioneer and inventor. It could easily have been the end of Herbert Dow. But it wasn't. He simply gave up working in Midland and set out to try again.

INTERLUDE IN NAVARRE: DOW AND CHLORINE

IT HAS NEVER BEEN CLEARLY KNOWN WHY HERBERT DOW CHOSE NAVARRE, A small town hundreds of miles away in Ohio, as the scene of his next venture. It may well be that he chose Navarre because it *was* hundreds of miles from Midland, where his disagreement with his directors about the possibilities of chlorine had made him an uncomfortably marked man. There is also the very good chance that he wanted to work out his chlorine process without too watchful an audience.

In fact, his first move after staking out the site of his little Navarre bleach plant was to surround it with a solid board fence eight feet high and with one door. All transactions, including deliveries, had to be made outside this door; no one not on Herbert Dow's five-man pay roll was permitted to set foot inside it, nor was the small plant ever left unguarded. Considering there was as yet no working process to guard, and that very few people knew enough chemistry in those days to understand the process if there had been one, this elaborate secrecy seems a bit premature. The fact is, however, that chemical companies in those days guarded even their most elementary practices as atomic secrets are guarded now, and Herbert Dow was only playing the accepted game. Indeed, he gave the game a touch of grim humor: he assured inquirers he was making embalming fluid, and this usually quenched all thirst for details.

What Dow was actually doing inside his board fortress did not, in fact, become generally known until years later.[1] Then the process he had been trying to work out emerged as a basic activity of The Dow Chemical Company, and eventually made it the world's largest single producer of chlorine.

---

[1] With the passing of time there has been a tendency to confuse Dow's Canton and Navarre activities. Canton was in 1889 and 1890, was Dow's first commercial venture, and concerned bromine. Navarre was in 1895 and 1896; he had "proved" his bromine process and was now working on chlorine.

At Navarre, for the first time in his life, Dow was not working with natural brine. He was buying salt, dissolving it in water, and attempting to electrolyze the solution so as to obtain two useful products at once. One of these was, of course, chlorine, which he proposed to treat with slaked lime to make chloride of lime—that is, bleach. The other proposed product was sodium hydroxide, familiarly known as caustic soda and much used in the manufacture of soap, glass, and other products. Thus the young man was trying, with the ebullience of the pioneering spirit, to make two chemicals at once before he had shown he could make one of them.

We know of this two-product objective through these opening paragraphs of the partnership agreement signed in 1895:

1. Herbert H. Dow, James T. Pardee, Albert W. Smith, J. H. Osborn and Cady Staley hereby agree to associate themselves as partners under the firm name of Dow Process Company, for the manufacture of and dealing in bleach and caustic under the process discovered and invented by Herbert H. Dow.

2. Herbert H. Dow agrees to furnish $2,000; James T. Pardee, $5,333.33; Albert W. Smith, $3,333.33; J. H. Osborn, $4,000; and Cady Staley, $2,000; all in money, to the capital of the partnership.

3. And Herbert H. Dow agrees to transfer and assign to the partnership his entire invention and discovery and process for the manufacture of bleach and caustic, together with any and all improvements he may make in said process....

Of these men who backed young Dow in his new venture, the reader already knows the faithful J. H. Osborn. Cady Staley was at the time president of Case School of Applied Science. Pardee was a civil engineer and a Case classmate of Dow's; he served many years as a director and treasurer of the present Dow Chemical Company, which grew out of the Dow Process Company we are discussing here.[2] A. W. Smith was a professor at Case and one of the best technical advisers and "recruiting sergeants" a company ever had: he helped Herbert Dow work out many difficult chemical problems, and helped obtain for him as young men such future stalwarts of The Dow Chemical Company as Thomas Griswold, Jr., Dr. E. O. Barstow, Dr. C. J. Strosacker, Dr. W. R. Veazey, Dr. Mark E. Putnam, and many others.

It is not known how Herbert Dow got back from the Midland Chemical Company, which still had ownership of it, the proposed process on which his new Dow Process Company was based. The only clue is a faded entry in the minute book of the Midland Chemical Company. The entry was

[2] Carl Gerstacker, Pardee's nephew, later became treasurer and a director.

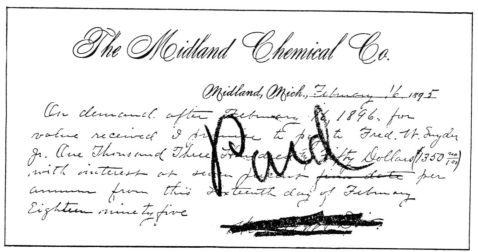

Sample of the demand notes to which Herbert Dow often resorted to keep his early ventures running. This one put the interest at only seven per cent; many he signed were for ten.

made soon after the chlorine explosion previously referred to, and it was to the effect that if Dow's chlorine process could not be sold to some other manufacturer, he was to have the use of it for one tenth of any gross receipts it brought in. Inasmuch as he was half of the two-man committee told off by the Midland Chemical Company directors to try to peddle it elsewhere, it is likely that at least half the committee did not try very hard to do so. It is also likely, by the way, that Dow did not expect to sell much bleach or caustic from Navarre. Apparently what he was actually doing was setting up a "pilot" or "semi" plant in which to work his process into manufacturing order—a project that was by no means to succeed overnight.

During the six or seven months of the Navarre venture, Dow and his growing family lived in the small town of Massillon, seven miles from Navarre. Dow commuted to and from work by his favorite method of transport, the bicycle. This he rode along the towpath of the Ohio-Erie Canal, which passed by his little plant and which has long since been filled in. Even while working at Navarre, three hundred miles from Midland, he meticulously attended the directors' meetings of the Midland Chemical Company at Midland. Indeed, search of the minute books of the company reveals he was the one director who never missed a single meeting. There were probably two reasons for this laudable attendance record. One was Dow's innate conscientiousness. The other was his eagerness at all times to defend his notions of what a chemical company should be and do—notions which did not always agree with those of his fellow-directors of the Midland Chemical Company.

Dow had not been many weeks at Navarre when he began getting disquieting letters from his four backers. It was pretty much the old story: the men who were putting up the money could not understand why a chemical process that works without a hitch on paper should not do the same in a factory—and start in at once to make them some money. Here is a typical nudge from Pardee, who seems to be voicing the disappointment of the four men behind Dow:

DEAR DOW,—I have refrained from writing you for some time in hope of receiving some encouraging news regarding the progress you were making in the work. I have felt so discouraged over the way things turned out, that I haven't felt like thinking about it long enough to write. I thought from what you said that we would be able to start up right away and make some bleach, but it seems from what you have written Dr. Smith that you are not able even to get chlorine part of the time. . . .

Another occupational hazard that Dow had to live with at Navarre took the form of a local citizen who had been a chemist in Europe. European chemists were supposed (especially by Europeans) to be about all the chemists there were, and this man enjoyed great local prestige. He saw Dow's arrival in Navarre as a threat to his glamour, but offered to give the young man the benefit of his chemical knowledge anyway. Dow formed the notion he was one of the spies with which the budding American chemical industry of the day abounded; he would not let the man in the plant or even talk to him. This made the man pretty mad, and he circulated rumors that Dow and his makeshift chlorine plant were a menace to life and limb. Dow did not appreciate this form of heckling, especially as it had some basis in truth. He was in the little cell room one day, for instance, when an explosion filled the room with chlorine and laid him unconscious. A workman saved his life by kicking a couple of boards out of the side of the building and dragging him into the open air.

After about six months at Navarre, Dow went back to Midland. No one knows quite why. The most logical guess is that he found his proposed plan for making chlorine and caustic from water and salt harder and less economical than he had expected. It would be better, he apparently concluded, to forget about caustic for the moment, and concentrate on his original plan of getting chlorine from natural brine. In any case, he arrived back in Midland early in 1896, at age thirty.

HOME TO MIDLAND:
DOW MAKES BLEACH

Dow's first move on returning to Midland was to set up a small bleach plant on a patch of land leased from the Midland Chemical Company. That company was still interested only in bromine, which it was recovering from brine by the process Dow had developed. It therefore looked on its debrominated brine—that is, brine from which the bromine had been removed—as so much waste material. Dow was able to arrange to buy this "waste" cheaply; still operating as the Dow Process Company, he now settled down to obtaining its chlorine to turn into bleach. It was this very project which had so much upset his fellow directors of the Midland Chemical Company only a few months before.

This time Dow made his process work. It still contained many "bugs" or imperfections, but Dow was sure he could iron these out—as indeed he eventually did. There was one problem, however, to which there could be only one answer. To make any money from bleach, he would have to produce it in volume; to get his process into volume production he would need a considerably larger plant. This called, of course, for more capital—and so he went to Cleveland again in search of more capital. Though his record to date contained many frustrations, he could also point to some real successes. He was the first man in the world to obtain bromine in commercial quantities by electrolysis, and his process was paying its backers substantial dividends. There was every indication that he would be able to repeat on chlorine, and make his backers money with that, too.

In any event, this invitation was soon going out on the letterhead of The East End Savings Bank Company of Cleveland to local business men:

You are cordially invited to meet a number of other representative business men at this office on Tuesday, May 4th, 1897, at 7:30 standard time. Professor A. W. Smith of Case School and Mr. H. H. Dow, secretary of the Midland Chemical Company, will be present to explain a new process of manufacture.

At the meeting was circulated the prospectus of a proposed new company to be known as The Dow Chemical Company.[1] It is probable that Dow and Charles Post of the East End Bank wrote the prospectus between them. The following excerpt from a section labeled "General Remarks" gives an idea of what the two men had in mind. However, as we shall presently see, the fourth and sixth paragraphs were to prove a bit over-optimistic. The prophecy of no decrease in prices in Paragraph 4 was later to fall on its face with a vengeance and almost put the new company out of business. Paragraph 6 was particularly cheerful in assuming that Herbert Dow's method of making chlorine was "extremely simple" and had been worked out in detail:

GENERAL REMARKS

About $2,000,000.00 worth of Chloride of Lime or Bleaching Powder is consumed each year in the U. S., but none is now made here on a Commercial Scale.

We propose to manufacture it by a new electrical process, in some respects similar to our Bromine process that has proven a phenomenal success.

We are the first persons, so far as any records show, to make use of electricity in any chemical manufacture, on a commercial scale aside from the electroplating of metals. This is quite a different operation and has been in use for many years.

Bleach is made from Lime and Chlorine, the latter obtained from the Chloride of natural Salt brines. Chlorine and Bromine are very Similar Substances and from a commercial standpoint both are peculiar in that there is no tendency towards decreasing prices. . . .

In the design of plant figured upon it will be possible to run 350 days per year without any one individual working more than six days per week. . . .

Our method of making Chlorine is extremely simple and does not require expensive apparatus and has been developed to such an extent that we advocate no change whatever even in size in the proposed new plant. . . .

The upshot of the meeting was that fourteen days later, that is, on May 18, 1897, the present Dow Chemical Company was organized. The new and larger organization took over the assets of the Dow Process Company; in 1900 it was also to take over the Midland Chemical Company.

President of the newly founded Dow Chemical Company was Albert E. Convers, a Cleveland manufacturer. He remained president until 1918,

---

[1] It may or may not be confusing to bear in mind that Herbert Dow was at the moment actively running the Dow Process Company, which was making bleach, and serving as secretary of the Midland Chemical Company, which was using his process to make bromine. Evidently the invitation had identified him with the Midland Chemical Company because that was known in Cleveland and was known to be making money.

First pay roll of The Dow Chemical Company, 1897. Apparently the black vertical line indicates when the Dow Process Company ended and the new company took over.

when he became chairman of the board, in which position he continued till his death in 1935. Vice-presidents of the new company were S. T. Wellman, a steel man, and G. E. Collings, a manufacturer of woolens. Secretary-treasurer was Charles A. Post, a banker. Herbert Dow was general manager; it was not till 1918 that he became also president. Sitting on the board of directors with these men were the Messrs. Staley, Smith, Pardee, Osborn, whom we already know as perennial backers of Dow, and A. L. Fuller and William L. Baker, a Midland banker. It is an interesting coincidence that the year 1897, when The Dow Chemical Company started, saw also the birth of Willard H. Dow, who in 1930 succeeded his father as active head of the company.

From the beginning, The Dow Chemical Company differed in important ways from all previous Dow-inspired enterprises. For one thing, it started out with a fairly comfortable capitalization of $200,000. This was divided into 20,000 shares of $10 par value each. Another important difference was in the spread of stock ownership. The Dow Chemical Company began with no less than 57 original stockholders, as against the 6 that the Midland Chemical Company had begun with. As general manager, Herbert Dow was to be the man on the ground actually running the company: it is likely that he had a very great deal to do with this spread of ownership. He had had his portion of being thwarted in his ideas by one or two big stockholders.

Meanwhile, construction of the new company's plant was getting under way at Midland. Allotted to the young general manager for this purpose was $83,333.33. Compared to his previous experiences that was a very generous allowance: it was a great deal more money than the young man had ever had to build with before. The fact is, however, that this sum had to be stretched to cover cost of land, design, building materials, actual building, and purchase and installation of equipment—some of it pretty expensive equipment.

From all surviving accounts, the designing and building of the new plant had all the enthusiasm and confusion of a crusade getting started. Nowadays industrial companies call in outsiders to do much of this for them; Herbert Dow and a few men he gathered about him did every inch of the designing and building themselves. Economy was not a mere watchword: it was an obsession. No building material was even remotely considered if cheap local lumber would *possibly* do—and this meant *possibly*. Where this lumber would have to stand up to escaping chlorine, it was liberally daubed with cheap tar. So were roofs; outside walls were not painted, but covered with a mixture of skimmed milk and cement, which was cheaper. Nails were economized on; things like windows and doors, which are ordinarily bought, were made on the spot—of cheap local lumber. Working hours ranged from twelve to sixteen a day, with no thought of "overtime." Thomas Griswold, a young engineer just out of Case School, was a member of this small and inspired band of enthusiasts; so was Herbert Dow's father, who had come on the job as a sort of combination designer, hammer-and-saw man, and elder statesman. Mr. Griswold, who after a half century or so of active work with the company he helped to set up is still a consulting engineer for it, recalls vividly both the enthusiasm and the grim insistence upon economy:

Herbert Dow was highly ingenious in devising novel processes, and means for carrying them out. His obsession for wood and tar was notorious and designs had to be executable with saw, hammer and square. Iron work was permitted rarely and only when he could not contrive something of wood assumed to be equally good.

The power house, lime slaker and pump house were built of brick, all other buildings of wood. Some two weeks of argument were spent on the question of type of power house. Herbert's father and I held out for brick against Herbert's choice of wood or corrugated iron on a wood frame. Brick was used, practically over Herbert's dead body.

Of the various buildings constructed, perhaps the masterpieces of young Dow's economy engineering were the nine "cell houses." These buildings were to house the cells which would actually take the chlorine out of the brine. Each building was 40 ft. wide by 90 ft. long. Structural members were mostly 16-foot cedar poles bought by the raft right out of the Tittabawassee River, which flowed by the plant. Boards were often local hemlock of the grade that railroads in those days used to fence in their right of way. Also used was a great deal of "dri-ki"—pinkish pine boards sawed from local dead timber on burned-over land. Each of the nine buildings, complete, cost $500—that is, 14 cents per square foot of floor space. Even in those days, that was a mouth-wateringly low cost for productive factory space. Dow hoped these buildings would last ten years; some of them were still in use twenty years later. Today, over fifty years later, timbers from them are still on the job here and there about the Dow plant—still plain-looking in their coats of protective tar, and still serviceable as ever.

Another example of Herbert Dow's militant economy was the "lime house," where bought quicklime was to be slaked before being treated with chlorine to make bleach. Also highly economical was the "absorber house," 368 ft. long by 40 ft. wide, where the bleach was actually made.

But perhaps the supreme triumphs of aggressively frugal construction were the cells themselves. Electrochemistry was just beginning in this country, and it was a daring chlorine manufacturer, indeed, who would undertake to get this highly corrosive chemical by electrolysis from anything less than a porcelain or enamel cell, with platinum anodes and mercury cathodes. Dow had the requisite daring. His cells were long shallow troughs made of cheap, local, tarred lumber. Each cell was divided by wood-and-tar partitions into a procession of smaller cells or "traps." For electrodes he did not even consider using metal. Instead, he used round "pencils" of carbon which had been meant for the arc lamps of the day, but which had been culled out as imperfect and so could be bought for almost nothing. Each of these sticks of carbon served as both anode and cathode: they were set in holes in the trap partitions, and carried the current from the brine in one trap through to the brine in the other, and so from one end of the series of traps or small cells to the other. This of course saved expensive copper wiring—another economy which Dow had much in mind. It was with some pride that he was able to report to his stockholders that his whole bleach plant cost less to build than just the electrodes in some rival plants.

When it came to buying engines, boilers, or other power machinery, however, Dow simply had to have the best available, regardless of cost. A few years before, he had scoured the country for a 50-kilowatt generator, then about the largest being made. The manufacturers of electrical equipment had been making some progress meanwhile, and this time Dow was able to get his hands on a 400-kilowatt generator—a veritable giant in those days. To drive it he had specially built an engine that ran twenty-four hours a day for eighteen months without one shutdown. Condensers, pumps, and air compressor units were required to be of the same hardy constitution, regardless of cost. He intended his plant to run day and night, month in and month out, and without expensive "stand by" equipment. To do this the equipment had to be good.

Incidentally, this demand of Herbert Dow's for ever larger and more efficient power machinery never left him. He was all his life a chronic and expert needler of the manufacturers of electrical equipment, constantly demanding they build bigger and better. It was almost as if he felt they were asleep at their switches, or afraid to exhibit imagination, or even tacitly willing to let the expanding electrochemical industry mark time till they got around to expanding with it. Dow was very serious about this; he knew that, in general, the greater amount of power he could create at one time, the cheaper he could get each unit of it. This brought the matter of power onto his favorite stamping ground, economy of manufacturing methods—an area where he simply would not accept frustration. At the very end of his life, when he could find no one in this country to build him a generator of the special size and efficiency he demanded, he went over to Switzerland, explained what he wanted, and had it built there.

It should be mentioned that even while he was still a very young man, Dow's ideas for achieving bigger and better electrical equipment were by no means brushed aside lightly by the equipment manufacturing companies. Earl W. Bennett, the present board chairman, recalls that in 1902 the

Herbert Dow in 1897, when he founded the present Dow Chemical Company. He was 31 years old at the time, and had behind him seven or eight years of mingled success and frustration. He was later to discard his moustache; it is said he used it in order to make himself look older to prospective investors and customers. Always practical, he was already noted for the quantity and character of his ideas as well as for his perseverance.

Promotion material for one of Herbert Dow's earliest side ventures. The cyclist is thought to be Dow. The company was born and died in the spring of 1896. It made and sold a compound to be poured into bicycle tires to seal punctures from the inside. The venture collapsed when tire manufacturers removed their guarantee from any tire showing signs of having been filled with the stuff.

Dow's first bleach plant, at Navarre. Here he experimented for several months of 1896 on the element which was later to be the basis of much of his lifework—chlorine. Note the high fence around the little plant. This was to ward off Peeping Toms, with which the young chemical industry abounded. Even those who got into a secrecy-minded plant seldom learned anything useful. Instruments like thermometers and pressure gauges were often calibrated to give false readings; starting materials were frequently mislabeled, and similar ruses practiced.

Westinghouse Electric Company returned Dow's specifications for a generator he wanted built, with the news that no one could build it. Dow went to their plant and showed them how to build it. The result of this was that Westinghouse engaged him as a part-time consultant on the design and building of generators and turbines, for the then considerable fee of $1,000 a year. This arrangement continued till 1908. There is no doubt that Dow's preoccupation with matters of power stemmed from his boyhood discussions of turbines with his father.

Two other lifelong patterns of Herbert Dow's industrial thinking took permanent form in his early manhood, and cannot be overemphasized by anyone who wants really to understand him and his legacy to his company. One was his emphasis, already noted, on using readily available materials wherever possible. We have just seen him build his plant chiefly of cheap local lumber. For a long time local scrap wood fired its boilers. And throughout his life, the brines under Midland were its chief raw material.

Part of this attitude came, especially in these early days, from necessity: he had to "make do." But even in later years, when the outside pressure was off, he still had an inner need to do things with what was at hand. Late in his life it was proposed to build a new courthouse at Midland, and he was asked to take part in the project. He found to his horror that the stone for the courthouse was to be Vermont marble, the traditional stone for courthouses. By the time he got through expressing his thoughts on the subject, the builders used granite boulders from Midland County, with magnesite stucco made with magnesium from under the county.

Another lifetime policy laid down in these early days was dependence, wherever possible, on local labor. His plant was not built and run by artisans and mechanics drawn from distant industrial areas. Instead, young Dow chose to rely on men who had grown up on neighboring farms or in local lumber mills. These men, though not formally trained, had had actual experience with tools, mowers, reapers, threshing machines, portable engines, belts, pulleys, sprocket chains, and so on. They soon adapted themselves to work as carpenters, pipe fitters, engineers, and foremen. Herbert Dow always looked on these men and their work as just as important as what his chemists were doing in the laboratory; they knew he believed this because he spent so much time watching their work in the factory. Once, in later years, Dow learned that a workman who had grown old and infirm in his service was dreading the retirement that was awaiting him. Dow thought up the idea of having the man sit on a chair by one of the gates and greet fellow workmen as they passed in or out. The man sat there for years, feeling himself to be still an important cog in the company's operation—which was exactly what Herbert Dow felt he was entitled to feel.

BY THANKSGIVING DAY of 1897, though the plant was by no means completed, production of bleach was begun. Brine which had been stripped of its bromine arrived by pipe line from the Midland Chemical Company, a few hundred yards away. Fed into Dow's homemade wood-tar-and-carbon cells, the brine gave up chlorine, which passed on to the "absorber house," where it was reacted with slaked lime to make bleach.[2] The first bleach was sold on January 5, 1898; this was the first sale of product by The Dow Chemical Company. It was a small one; $37.48 worth of bleach. By the end of the first twelve months of operation, sales had amounted to $9,707.84, and The Dow Chemical Company was on a commercial basis.

Presently, however, the homemade electrolytic cells were beginning to act up in serious fashion. Two stockholders, Professor Smith of Case and Dr. Edward Morley, went to Midland to help diagnose the trouble. In a letter written on August 18, 1899, Dr. Morley reported:

We found the works in tolerably good condition. I do not think we are to have dividends very soon, though Mr. Smith is more hopeful than I was. . . . They have leaks that lose one-third of the current making chlorine, and lose one-third of the chlorine actually made by the remainder of the current. So we are just on the margin of profit, but not on the right side. Whenever an important source of loss is stopped, we shall have profits.

After some weeks of fruitless searching, the main sources of loss were apprehended and corrected. From long contact with brine and chlorine, both of which are extremely corrosive, many of the boards which held the carbon electrodes had become spongy and porous. This permitted current to pass through without making chlorine. Many of the carbon electrodes, too, had become porous. Hydrogen gas was seeping along from one end of the electrode, and meeting the chlorine gas forming at the other. The resultant explosions, some mild and some pretty violent, were using up chlorine and often wrecking the traps besides. Spongy boards were replaced; the electrodes were impregnated with paraffin. At the height of the trouble, the plant had been losing $163 a day. This loss was wiped out and the plant

[2] The process was supposed to be automatic and continuous—and it eventually was. But at first so many things went wrong (or did not go at all) that an eye-witness remarked that the "automatic" process needed half the manpower of Midland County to keep it going at all—let alone continuously.

went back into the black. Herbert Dow asked his directors for money to double the plant's capacity. This was granted, and in 1900 capacity and output were doubled. The following year, they were doubled again.

This success of the wood-and-tar cells justified increasing the company's capitalization to $500,000 and then to $850,000. Of the latter amount, $300,000 was used to buy out the Midland Chemical Company, which a few years before had been so pointedly unresponsive to Dow's idea of getting chlorine from the debrominated brine it was throwing away. This put the young chemist and his team back at the helm of his bromine process, which he had worked through years of frustration to invent and perfect.

Years later Leland I. Doan, who in 1949 succeeded Herbert Dow's son as president of The Dow Chemical Company, pointed out:

With some duplication of stockholders and directors an eventual merger was probably inevitable. But I think it is significant that when the merger came, in 1900, it was the more enterprising Dow Chemical that absorbed the original corporation, rather than the other way around.

There is more to this observation than meets the eye. Both these companies had been physically constructed by Herbert Dow. Both used processes which he worked out; both made a product for which there was a ready market. There was, in fact, only one real difference between them, and that was in attitude. The Midland Chemical Company was interested just in immediate profits. There was no interest in *growing*—in expanding the company's capacity, in venturing into new products, or in improving the manufacturing processes. There was not even an interest in the routine amenities of plant housekeeping. A typical outward and visible sign of this shortsighted attitude was a hole six feet long in the roof of one of the buildings, which remained unrepaired while the stockholders voted themselves monthly dividends. It is not hard to see why one company went on and the other did not.

IF THIS SUCCESS of the young team went to its head, that certainly did not show up on the pay roll. A pay list of January, 1901, shows that Thomas Griswold, graduate engineer, was drawing $19.18 a week. E. O. Barstow, graduate chemist and eventual vice-president and director, was down for $13.80. Earl W. Bennett, bookkeeper and eventual chairman of the board, drew $11.50. Dow himself, an older man whose brain child the whole enterprise was, drew only $57.53 a week. The Dow team was out to make chemicals, not a quick financial killing.

8

HOUSE AND GARDEN

MEANWHILE, HERBERT DOW HAD BEEN BUILDING HIMSELF A HOME AND A family. In 1892, at age twenty-six, he had married Miss Grace Anna Ball, daughter of G. Willard and Amelia Eaton Ball. Mr. Ball was a Midland merchant and had helped found Midland's first bank. Like the Dows, the Balls were descended from early English settlers of New England: the original Ball had settled there in 1635.

The affection in which Herbert Dow held his wife's family is indicated by his naming his first son Willard for Mr. Ball. Another son was named Alden Ball in honor of the Balls and of John Alden, another New England ancestor. Another son, who died when a little boy, was named Osborne, for one of Herbert Dow's most loyal backers. There were also four daughters: Helen, Ruth Alden, Margaret Grace, and Dorothy Darling. Also living in Midland were Herbert Dow's father and mother, Joseph and Sarah Dow, and Helen and Mary Dow, Herbert's sisters.

To house his pleasantly numerous family, the young man needed rather a large home, and he built one near the plant. This was in 1899, and was the first and last home he was to build. He had been born in Canada, grew up in Connecticut and Cleveland, and started companies at Canton, Navarre—and Midland. Now he was to spend the rest of his life living and working in Midland.

From the mass of correspondence which survives on the subject, it would appear that the designing and building of Herbert Dow's house gave the architects, contractors, materials suppliers, and workmen a pretty brisk workout. He insisted the house be designed and built in accord with the ideas by which he built his plant; if there was a detail of design or execution that had escaped his alert eye and attention, it is hard to imagine what that detail could be. For months on end letters, blueprints, and plans traveled back and forth between Dow and the architects, introducing this feature and taking that one out. A laundry chute which Mrs. Dow had her heart set on made a tour of the proposed premises, finally coming to rest where it had started. Dormer windows were inserted, removed, made bigger, made smaller, and shifted all over the roof. The roof kept being tilted this way and that. At one point the whole house as planned got turned end for end: the porte-cochère forgot to switch with the rest of the building, and was left for the moment embellishing the kitchen door. There were long debates about heating and plumbing arrangements, with careful attention to the danger of pipes freezing in winter, a thing not unknown in central Michigan. Meanwhile, in accord with Herbert Dow's philosophy of using Midland workers and materials wherever possible, the hunt was on to locate them. The opening gun of this campaign was a letter to a neighboring farmer on April 20, 1899:

Have you any cobble stones you wish to sell? If so, I will pay $1.10 for every good two-horse load delivered on my lot on Main Street near the Upper Bridge, until I have received 100 loads.

A week or so later, Dow was writing the architects:

We have had several men at work for some days taking out pine stumps, putting in drains, water connections, etc. We have been able to get but little stone thus far, as the farmers who usually bring in stone are very busy just at present. If the house can be gotten under way without all the stone being in place, it might be an advantage.

A few weeks later Dow had the stone but not enough men to lay it. He accordingly wrote to a Mr. Jakes, a stonemason of near-by Freeland:

DEAR SIR: We can use two or three good stone masons in addition to the ones we have on the house I am building in Midland near the Upper Bridge. There is still about thirty cords of stone to lay. If you or your brother are at liberty to help us in this work, we will be glad to have you start in as soon as possible. We pay $2.00 a day to most men, but if you are worth more to us than the men we now have, we will increase this price.

By September, his attention was on plumbing supplies and hardware, and he wrote to the architects:

If you have the hardware specifications, I wish you would send them to me, and I will attend to the buying. *So far in the construction of this house I have not seen a specification for anything.* . . . I will not order until investigating, although it should have been attended to a month or more ago, and we have not time to lose.

This got straightened out the next day, whereupon Dow wrote back that the painting was not being done as he had ordered. The details he gave indicated that it was being done exactly as he ordered it—a piece of news which was relayed to him with the tactful comment that "We fear your last letter was written on the impulse of the moment." Even at age thirty-three, which Herbert Dow was then, it was not a good idea to be tactless in demonstrating to him that he was wrong about something.

A last hitch developed several weeks later. One of the bathroom fixtures kept running; Dow, in attempting to fix it, had made it worse. "If it is convenient for you to come up here," he wrote the plumbing contractor, "it would probably be better for you to fix it than for me to fool with it." It is to be hoped the man came: despite all the ingenious machinery Herbert Dow thought up, it was a standing (but secret) joke among his colleagues that he could not handle any but the simplest tool without damaging himself or the job.[1] In any event, by November of 1899 he was writing his friend Professor Smith: "We are just beginning to move in our new house. We will probably change our place of sleeping Monday or Tuesday."

Incidentally, the house was built for convenience and comfort rather than show; nor did Herbert Dow change it or build again when he became widely known and comparatively well-to-do. Especially in his later years, when important industrialists and chemists from all over the world came to see him, surprise was often expressed that so successful a man should be living in such an unpretentious house. This was part of the plainness and directness of character which Herbert Dow never changed; he never, as successful people sometimes unhappily do, adopted the airs, graces, and "side" that are occasionally thought to be required of the successful. In company he acted like anyone else, except that he never developed much of a knack for small talk. He liked jokes and comical stories, but never could learn to tell them; he had the rare good sense to give up trying. Among associates and friends he was apt to talk chemistry, mechanics, economics, and industrial philosophy. Many of his ideas in these fields were highly original, and he liked nothing better than a brisk argument about them. He liked also to

---

[1] It took Herbert Dow some time to digest the fact that his hands did not share his brain's adeptness in mechanical matters. He spent much time in the factory, and he was years learning not to snatch tools from workmen's hands to show how they should be used. On one such occasion he undertook to show how a roof should be tarred, tarred himself into the middle of it, and had to be rescued via an improvised catwalk.

sing; it was the day of the barbershop quartet, and his prowess around the family piano was well known.

Starting at this time and continuing to the end of his life, Frank Teal's barbershop over on Main Street served Herbert as a sort of combination social club and debating forum. He dropped in every morning for a shave and, if possible, an argument. Sometimes he would come back in the afternoon or the evening for a new argument or to extend his remarks on the one of the morning. Often these discussions served as a sort of obbligato to a game of checkers, a pastime of which he was very fond. He also liked to play checkers (and argue) with the men at the town firehouse and with his own workmen during lunch hour at the plant.

Stating Herbert Dow's forthrightness so frankly may make him appear self-centered. It is true that his mind was much on his ideas and his work, but he was also a devoted family man. In 1901 he wrote enthusiastically to a friend: "You ought to see my family. A two-seated carriage will hold them if they are two deep." Some time after that, and after years of marriage, he wrote to a friend that he could not attend a convention of scientists because it would keep him away from his wife and children on a Sunday. He had, he added, been away only two Sundays since he was married, and did not propose to be away a third if he could help it. His letters to friends often mention the antics of his small children; in his correspondence on weighty chemical matters, items crop up like this "Prescription for feeding a well baby one year old":

Cream 2 oz., Milk 2 oz., Lime-Water 1 oz., Water 3 oz., Milk Sugar ½ oz. This to be heated together to about 180° F. in a water bath for 5 or 10 minutes.

With his house completed and his numerous brood installed in it, Herbert Dow launched himself on what was to be his lifelong hobby. This was the development and care of gardens and orchards. His original estate was ten acres of sandy soil covered with jack pine. The land was not, as it stood, suitable for growing much of anything but more jack pine. He seemed to see this fact as a sort of personal challenge, and during the rest of his life he added to his holdings at the rate of forty acres or so at a time, and set much of it out in gardens and orchards. As early as 1902 he was writing to Mr. Osborn:

My hobby is fruit trees, and we have more than a hundred varieties in our back lot. The Japan plums seem to be the most phenomenal trees we have. I have nearly forty varieties of plums.

Within a few years he had over five thousand fruit trees growing up out of the sandy soil. He liked to speak of this arrangement as "my golf course," and he was determined that it should pay its own way. It never did, at least directly: he was so intent on raising every possible variety of plum, pear or apple that he never had enough of any one kind to send to market. Also the trees, aside from bearing fruit, were required to serve as guinea pigs for various chemicals Herbert Dow thought might encourage them in one way or another. This was to an extent the start of the company's interest in agricultural chemicals, of which it now sells some eighteen or twenty million dollars' worth a year.

Another form of chronic experimentation that Herbert Dow indulged in was aimed at feeding the trees' roots most effectively. He was, after all, trying to raise fruit on sandy, not very fertile soil. He finally hit on the idea of piling what top soil there was up close to each tree, with the result that each tree occupied a sizable private hummock. This did make the fruit better, but made it very difficult to plant and cut hay or get spray machinery between the rows. Dow took this very calmly, though the men who had to operate the haying and spraying machinery looked on each orchard as a sort of deliberate obstacle course. However, as Herbert Dow spent hours at a time, especially on Sundays, shoveling more dirt up on the hummocks, they learned to be philosophical about it.

It was Herbert Dow's enthusiasm for fruit raising that brought him into correspondence with men like Luther Burbank and Dr. U. P. Hedrick, of the New York State Experimental Station at Geneva. Agriculture was just then becoming scientific, and Dr. Hedrick believed that Dow had missed his vocation by becoming an industrial chemist instead of a full-time agriculturist. He liked Dow's challenging willingness to try anything that showed any prospect of working, and his cheerful acceptance of frustration when what looked like a very good idea failed to pan out. Some of these frustrations were on the humorous side. Typical of these was his scheme to outwit the robins who annually cleaned out his strawberry patch before he could get any berries to speak of for himself. Dow's approach had the grandeur of simplicity: he enlarged his strawberry patch to the extent that he was sure there would be enough for all the robins in Midland, with some left over for him. This turned out to be a sad instance of the law of diminishing returns: the bigger the patch got, the more robins showed up and the fewer berries were left. Dow could never decide whether the additional robins were authentic Midland residents, or immigrants from the neighboring countryside who had got wind of the lush pickings. In any case, he gave up the scheme as a bad job. He liked to say that his success in life was in part the result of his being right fifty-two times out of a hundred, and wrong only forty-eight. He accepted this as one of the forty-eight.

Another of the forty-eight was his plan to make seven hundred dollars an acre on muskmelons. This project blew up by a process of violent inflation: he got so many melons at once that he overwhelmed his prospective market and had to give them away at the plant and in town by the wagonload.

Almost as much of Herbert Dow's spare-time attention went to his grounds and flower gardens. Here, as in the case of his orchards, he had only extremely poor sandy soil to work with, but he met the challenge and in time produced a real miracle of natural beauty. Plants, shrubs, and trees were brought in from far and near and arranged to produce original and pleasing effects. Informal vistas and unexpected patches of beauty were created, giving a feeling of freedom and naturalness, as against the sense of confinement and blueprinting often conveyed by formalized landscaping.

In addition Dow created, by repeatedly dredging and altering the course of a small stream that ran through the grounds, a pleasingly asymmetrical network of pools, estuaries, waterfalls, and lagoons. Here again the idea was to delight the eye by the original and creative, rather than offer the commonplace and traditional.

Doing all this seemed to give Dow an outlet for his original and creative nature, in addition to chemistry; it was probably an added pleasure to him to create beauty out of plainness. The lumber industry, in departing from Midland, had not left it exactly a beauty spot, and Herbert Dow spent a great deal of time, thought, and money in encouraging the whole community to go in for gardening. He was a leading spirit in the Midland Garden Club, and put up most of its prizes. To a banker curious about this interest in flowers and gardens he wrote:

Our Garden Club work in Midland is not similar to that of many flower and garden clubs where prizes are offered for the best specimens. Our work is directed towards making artistic gardens and beautiful homes with harmonious surroundings, and our prizes are offered for artistic gardens, lawns and neat premises, rather than for fine individual specimens of flowers.

For years Dow served without pay as the town's superintendent of parks, and maintained the parks out of his own pocket. He also served for years on the town's board of education, and kept the town's churches, regardless of denomination, painted at his expense. In later life he was active in founding a country club, a community center, and other communal activities. Years after his death a national magazine called Midland "The Town a Test Tube Built," and praised it as a sort of model community for gardens, modern educational system, discussion and cultural clubs, and other facilities for pleasant and enlightened living. Especially noted was the town's spirit of freedom from intellectual, social, or income-based snobbery. Though he kept himself in the background, Herbert Dow had a great deal to do with all this.

9

THE BATTLE OF THE BLEACH

THE PROSPERITY OF THE RISING YOUNG DOW CHEMICAL COMPANY WAS BASED firmly on two chemical elements: bromine and chlorine. Brine, the raw material for both of these, was to be had for the pumping from under the plant and the surrounding countryside. Thanks to Dow's economical wood-and-tar cells, it did not cost much to make this cheap raw material give up its bromine and chlorine. These went to market as bromides and bleach, and the little company was selling all of them it could make.

The original bleach plant built by Herbert Dow in 1897 made nine tons of bleach a day. By 1902, as the result of plant enlargements and process improvements, Dow was making and selling seventy-two tons a day. Most of this was going to the paper pulp mills of Michigan, Wisconsin, Minnesota, and western Ohio. Up till late in the previous century, the chief uses of bleach had been as a disinfectant and in the textile industry. But the linotype machine and the rotary printing press had been invented; these called for more and cheaper paper to print on than the traditional rags could supply. Dozens of mills sprang up to make cheap and plentiful paper from wood pulp; these plants required vast tonnages of bleach to turn the pulp from wood-color to white.

Up to a few years before, all the bleach used in this country had come from English plants, which had charged what they chose for it. But now Dow and other domestic producers had come on the market; and, with the widening usefulness of bleach, it was becoming a highly competitive market. Dow found most of his customers in the Michigan-Wisconsin-Minnesota-Ohio area because his location gave him a competitive advantage there.

On the face of things, American bleach manufacturers had a great advantage over competition from abroad. English bleach had to cross the ocean, which meant freight charges; it had to pay duty at port of entry; it had to be loaded on trains for shipment into the interior, which meant more freight charges. Furthermore, it lost "available" chlorine during this repeated handling and thousands of miles of travel, and chlorine is the useful part of the bleach.[1] American bleach, on the other hand, could be loaded in boxcars right at the plant, and arrive in anywhere from one to a few days at the customer's plant. It took time, of course, to convince some bleaching foremen that the American product was as good as the foreign. But that was a problem that Dow had in common with rival pioneers in American bleach-making, and was soon pretty well solved. By 1902, then, when Dow was making his seventy-two tons of bleach a day, his competitive picture was pretty much one of convincing customers that his bleach was as good or better than the traditional English product.

But what could have been a fatal battle was brewing—in fact had been brewing under the surface for the past six or eight years. For several reasons, it is of interest here to look into the origin, course, and outcome of the struggle. Though the battle, superficially looked at, seems to have been only about bleach, it was in reality a struggle between the traditional "old" and the venturesome "new" in the world's chemical industry. Had this fight and a few others like it gone differently, the industry as a whole would have lost years in its march to becoming the spiritedly creative and humanly useful activity it is today. The battle helped decide, too, whether this country would develop a strong, creative, and independent chemical industry of its own—or would have to rely on in peace, and fear in war, the chemical industries of other nations. Finally, and no less importantly in Herbert Dow's mind, the battle was to decide whether young companies like his were to go on existing, creating, and growing—or go out of business.

Traditionally, bleach prices were announced in December, when contracts were drawn up for the ensuing twelve months. Until domestic manufacturers like Dow began preparing to enter the picture, the English had usually set the price at $3.50 a hundredweight—a ridiculously high figure. In the middle nineties, with the threatened American competition be-

---

[1] Like bromine, chlorine requires careful handling: it is highly volatile stuff and always trying to get away. For years, the most practicable way of shipping it was to "fix" it as bleach—that is, chloride of lime. The only usefulness of the lime was to hold onto as much as possible of the chlorine till the chlorine was needed. Today liquid chlorine, chlorine gas put under pressure and shipped in cylinders, does many of the jobs formerly assigned to bleach—such as bleaching paper pulp and disinfecting city water supplies.

coming an actuality, the English were setting their price around $1.87—an abrupt reduction of almost one half. That was the figure while Dow was building his plant in 1897, and the figure with which he was expecting to compete. Just as his plant was getting into production, the English lowered their price again, to $1.65. Competing with this figure left Dow very little margin for profit, but by dint of expanding his wood-and-tar plant and improving his process, he managed to make out pretty well. In fact, it was during this time that his production went from nine tons a day to seventy-two.

Meanwhile, abroad, things were happening that were soon going to have violent repercussions thousands of miles away in Midland. These European events were in fact a facet of the struggle between the "old" and the "new" in the world's chemical industry. The nub of the matter was this:

England had always been the traditional home of bleach-making, largely because it was also the traditional home of the textile industry, which up to the 1890's had been the only consumer of bleach in any volume.

Forty-odd alkali plants scattered through England, Scotland, and Wales were making practically all of this bleach. Curiously enough, they were not making it as a prime product. They were making it from chlorine incidentally obtained in the manufacture of their alkali—soda ash made for the textile, soap, and glass industries. This soda ash they were making by the Leblanc process, which dated from the time of the French Revolution. The process was aggressively cumbersome and awkward, but it had survived for a century because no one had worked out a better one.

Then, over in Belgium, somebody did work out a better one. This was the Solvay process; soon soda ash made by it was being sold in England and on the world markets at less than soda ash could be made for by the Leblanc process. This did not at first perturb the English soda-ash manufacturers much. What if they did lose money on soda ash made by their time-honored Leblanc process? They were, after all, still making a killing on their chlorine by-product—and the big profits there more than made up for the lowered prices on soda ash.

However, by 1890, it began to sink in that the Leblanc process was heading for serious trouble from the newer and far more efficient Solvay process. Nowadays, when a chemical company finds one of its basic processes decisively "trumped," it fights back by improving the process, or finding a better one, or forgetting the whole thing and manufacturing something else. This is one of the ways in which the chemical industry—or indeed any industry—progresses in usefulness. But the urge to progress was then pretty new, and the English soda-ash manufacturers elected to fight back by defending their outmoded process. To do this the English plants banded together to form the United Alkali Company, capitalized at millions of pounds. This huge aggregation, it was felt, would by sheer strength overpower the relatively small and scattered pioneers of the Solvay process, and—by no means incidentally—keep the individual bleach producers from cutting bleach prices below cost and thus starting a downward spiral in bleach prices.

The keystone in this defensive position was the price of bleach. Solvay-processed soda ash could still be undersold provided the profits on by-produced bleach stayed inflated enough to make up the loss.

But now, as part of the march of chemical progress, a new blow fell. Chlorine as a bleach was becoming more and more useful and needed, and it was likely that a way would be sought to provide it at less than United Alkali's monopoly price of $3.50 a hundredweight. This way was presently found by electrochemists in Germany and in America, Dow being typical of the latter group. It was to discourage these new bleach manufacturers that United Alkali had dropped its price to $1.87 and then to $1.65. As Herbert Dow put it years later:

> The reasoning that governed these prices is apparent; namely the United Alkali Company fixed the price in the United States at the highest figure they thought they could secure without bringing about competition. When they found competition was starting, they realized their American price ($3.50) was too high and they lowered it (to $1.87 and then to $1.65).

At about this point, in 1896, the chairman of the Society of the Chemical Industry of Great Britain commented:

> America has made wonderful progress during the last quarter of a century in mechanical devices mainly, but she is now turning her hand to chemicals, and a sad mess she has made already with English prices.... Anyone acquainted with the subject must know that the ordinary alkali trade, with high strength alkali at £25 per ton F.O.B., bleach at £6 and salt cake at 18/- is not change for a shilling.

This comment was curiously jaunty in view of the onslaught now to begin. The purpose was no longer to discourage rival bleach-makers like Dow, but to destroy them altogether. The American bleach market had for years been for the English soda-ash manufacturers a source of copious and succulent "gravy." Now, with huge profits from bleach required to keep the Leblanc soda-ash people going at all, the American bleach market was their bread, butter, and practically their existence.

Oddly enough, it was neither the English nor the Americans, the two principals, who touched off the real knock-down-and-drag-out phase of the battle. This service was rendered by a *third* interested party—the German chemical industry. Early in 1899, barely a year after The Dow Chemical Company had made its first small sale of bleach, Professor Smith wrote to Herbert Dow:

> In regard to the very low price of bleach, I much fear it is to be permanent and progressive and that the hope of large profits is over for us. Do you have the Eng. and Mining Journal? In the number of Feb. 4 is a statement by U. S. Consul Brundage at Aix la Chapelle, which says he has heard that a German firm had closed a contract for 4,000 tons of bleach to be put on board steamers for New York at $18.50 per ton, during 1899, to compete with English prices, tho' he said the price in Germany was 12 marks per 100 kilos. . . .
>
> From all this I am led to think that the struggle for the death of the English Alkali works is on in earnest, and that the Germans are the aggressors, and, further, that they are making their first big fight in our markets.

Once this gesture had got the fight started, the Germans pretty much withdrew from it. It was not the American bleach market they wanted: what they did want was the destruction of United Alkali's lush source of support there. If the resistance of men like Dow achieved this for them, their purpose was inexpensively served.

The actual blows of the attack, when they came, were as uncomplicated and to the point as shots fired from ambush. Late in 1902, United Alkali announced through its American agents that its 1903 price for bleach would be $1.25 per hundredweight, an undercutting of the going market by 40 cents. Obviously, United Alkali was going to lose money at $1.25, of which 20 cents was duty and at least some was ocean freightage. The point, of course, was that the vast combine could afford temporarily to lose money, and the small independents like Dow couldn't. The pressure was on to crowd them out of business—after which the price could be raised again.

Dow and his colleagues had just worked out plans to weather the storm when, a few weeks later, the English syndicate struck again. It had, its agents announced, reconsidered: instead of $1.25, its 1903 price for bleach would be $1.04. This was really a jolt. But Dow managed to hang on, and late in the year the syndicate delivered the blow that was expected to put him and the remaining domestic producers out of competition for good. Its price in 1904, the syndicate let it be known, would be 88½ cents—about half the price at which The Dow Chemical Company had been organized to do business. This was violent action, but still Herbert Dow would not give up. In fact, in his determination to go on fighting, he went out and signed contracts to sell practically all of his coming year's output at 86 cents.

This act of defiant courage brought the bleach war to an abrupt close. A few weeks after Dow had signed away his 1904 output at 86 cents, the English combine announced it had again reconsidered: its 1904 price for bleach would be $1.25. The other domestic producers had hung back; now they signed contracts at $1.25, too. Dow of course honored his 86-cent contracts, losing because of his courage some $90,000 in income that was sorely needed.

"It seems too bad," he wrote to a stockholder, "that we have to bear the entire cost of bringing the United Alkali Co. to its knees."

For years after that, the price of bleach stayed around $1.25, nor did United Alkali or anyone else ever again try to stampede Herbert Dow out of the bleach business. He stayed in it till nearly the time of World War I, when he began putting his chlorine to new uses. These uses, he hoped, would some day give the chlorine from his brine far more of an outlet than bleach ever would.

He turned out to be right. Today The Dow Chemical produces and uses right in its own plants millions of pounds of chlorine a day. Much of this goes into chlorinated products that are real triumphs of modern chemical ingenuity. In his bleach war with the English, Herbert Dow had been fighting about far more than some trainloads of bleach. He had been fighting about the future of his company and of the growing American chemical industry.

Dow plant in 1900. Note supply of cordwood for firing boilers.

Interior of early chlorine cell building. Not all the haze is due to primitive photography. Much of it is a fog of brine blown into the air by hydrogen escaping from the cells.

61

Early family group, photographed during visit to the California home of J. H. Osborn, one of the earliest and most persistent of Dow's backers. In the foreground are, left to right: Mrs. Dow; Ruth Dow; Willard H. Dow, who succeeded his father as head of the company in 1930; and Helen Dow. Herbert Dow is holding Osborne, who died in childhood. Mrs. Osborn sits in the rear; her husband was probably the photographer.

10

OUT OF THE COCOON

EXPANSION FROM A COMPANY MAKING JUST BLEACH AND POTASSIUM BROMIDE was by no means automatic and inevitable. Products and markets had to be found.

The first progress was with bromine. This progress became possible in 1900, when The Dow Chemical Company bought out the Midland Chemical Company, putting Herbert Dow back in charge of the bromine business he had started. In the four years during which he had had no say in the matter, the policy of manufacturing and marketing bromine had become a masterpiece of conservative simplicity. It was made and sold in just one form of one bromide—bromide of potash in crystals. The dozen or so other marketable compounds just were not bothered with, on the unenterprising theory that most customers were content with bromide of potash in crystals, and those who were not could shop elsewhere.

Herbert Dow soon changed that. A couple of years after he was back at the helm, he was writing to Mr. Osborn and mentioning with evident satisfaction his new bromine line, which was in fact rather complete for those days:

Bromide of Potash crystals	Bromide of Barium
Bromide of Potash granular	Bromide of Strontium
Bromide of Potash pulverized	Bromide of Iron
Bromide of Soda granular	Crude Bromide and Bromate of Soda
Bromide of Ammonia granular	Bromate of Potash
Bromide of Lithium	Liquid Bromine
Bromide of Calcium	Bromoform

"All these new things," Dow wrote, "have been gone into within about a year. We have found this necessary on account of having to supply the trade with a full line of bromides; otherwise they would depend upon our competitors."

Actually, he found at the time little sale for some of these chemicals, especially liquid bromine and bromoform; but still he insisted on having them available. Dow didn't like his customers even to think of depending on his competitors for anything he could possibly supply them, even though this attitude might cost considerable effort and pay no immediate profit. Today it is standard practice for major chemical companies to make dozens of small-selling products for the accommodation of customers or prospective customers. As Herbert Dow was among the first to foresee, it is one way a chemical company gets to be "major"—and have customers. Nor is it unknown for an unwanted chemical suddenly to become the belle of a very fine ball, in which happy event the company that already knows how to make it has the pleasure and profit of trotting it out on the floor to lead the grand march. Herbert Dow was to create dozens of chemical wallflowers, some of which got out on the floor in his lifetime and some after his death.

We shall soon be encountering some very important instances of this sort of thing. Such instances, and above all the spirit of enterprise and research behind them, were not the least of Dow's legacies to the company that bears his name. It is true that many of his explorations were carried on with the grudging consent and sometimes the open opposition of his early board of directors. Sometimes it will appear, on the surface, that Herbert Dow was an enterprising chemical genius being deliberately frustrated by a band of ultraconservative businessmen interested only in immediate profits. Like most generalizations, that is just true enough to be misleading. Dow was a businessman, too, and just as interested in profits as were his directors. The big difference was that he, as the company's general manager and man who knew chemistry, was the fellow right at the factory actually handling the chemicals. This put him in a position to see, or think he saw, possible products or processes that would make the company bigger, stronger—and more profitable. By contrast, most of the directors were Cleveland businessmen with little knowledge of the chemical industry, and little or no concept of its possibilities. Projects that to Herbert Dow looked like calculated risks that it would be senseless not to take often appeared to them, hundreds of miles away in Cleveland, as blind gambles it would be senseless to take. In time, these occasional gaps between Dow and his directors became less numerous and less pronounced. Here Dow's successes helped a great deal; so did the fact that more and more men with a knowledge of chemistry became directors. Dow's becoming president in 1918 just about settled the problem entirely.

With the above background in mind, we return to Herbert Dow's chronic search for new uses for the bromine and chlorine he was getting out of the brine. The enlargement of his line of pharmaceutical bromides has already been noted. At about the same time, Dow scented out and alertly pitched into a use for bromine that was for a while to enable him to sell more bromine than his pharmaceutical line did. Around 1900, a small order came in from Australia for an unfamiliar concoction of bromide and bromate of soda. Dow filled the order, and at the same time scouted around to see what the chemical was to be used for. It was, he found, being used in the gold-mining operations then so extensive in Australia. Crushed ore was saturated in a solution of the concoction; the bromine sought out the gold and formed bromide of gold, which was in turn easily reduced to pure gold. Dow saw a quantity use for his bromine and began mass-producing the preparation under the name of "mining salt." He sold a great deal in Australia and in Colorado, South Africa, and other gold-mining centers. This was Dow's first nonmedicinal use of bromine, and also his first product to go in quantity out of the country. From 1907 to 1911, his mining salt sales exceeded pharmaceutical sales. Use of this salt tapered off as better extraction methods were found, though as late as 1934, 150,000 pounds of it were shipped to Australia. Today the salt is no longer used for metal extraction, though a few hundred pounds are still sold each month for other purposes.

Incidentally, this mining salt caused the origin of the present "Dow Diamond" trademark. A workman who packaged the salt had also the job of marking each package with a painted DOW enclosed in a freehand rectangle. His rectangle slumped more and more towards the shape of a diamond, where it crystallized and became official—which it has been ever since.

Around the time of the mining salt boom, Dow got his bromine into another quantity market. Photography was then becoming very popular, and bromine in the form of silver bromide was coming into important use in the manufacture of film. The chief user was the Eastman Kodak Company at Rochester, New York. Dow, through his personal efforts, became the company's supplier, and "serviced the account" himself to the end of his days—long after he had set up a formal sales department within his own company.[1] He was in fact always quite proud of his connection with East-

[1] Dow's was one of the first chemical companies to develop its own sales department. Up till then it had been customary to sell to "factors," who in turn sold to the customers. Dow now has sales offices all over the country.

man. Though it came years after his battle to prove his bromides "pure," he looked on the connection as the final seal of approval.

These two nonpharmaceutical outlets for his bromine were to be of great aid and comfort to Herbert Dow in his looming fight with the German bromine trust, which will be described in the next chapter. Both outlets were found and developed by Dow in his role of alert businessman. A third outlet, which he tried to find and develop in his role of enterprising chemist, failed at the time but paid off a dozen years later. The organic branch of the German chemical industry, after years of effort, had succeeded in synthesizing indigo, the so-called "King of the Dyes," and was enjoying a world-wide monopoly in its manufacture and sale. Dow tried for about a year to develop a new indigo process but got nowhere with it. This was in 1906; in 1915 he resurrected his interest in synthetic indigo, and in 1916 his factory became the first in America to make this then difficult product.

Meanwhile, Dow had been beating the bushes to find outlets for chlorine other than chloride of lime, that is, bleach. Considering that less than a year before that The Dow Chemical Company had been set up to make bleach, it must have unsettled Professor Smith a bit to get this letter of March 9, 1898, from Herbert Dow:

I have an idea that we can make more money here out of sulphur chloride than out of most anything else. I understand it is the coming reagent in vulcanizing rubber, if so, we ought to be able to make it as cheap or cheaper than anyone else. . . . According to my best judgment at present there will be nothing so remunerative for us to take up in a new line as chloride of sulphur, but I know almost nothing about it.

In January of 1900, Dow was back on the subject. He wrote Professor Smith:

It now looks as though part of our chlorine could be made into sulfur chloride and a very much better price secured for it than we can get for it in the form of bleach.

Apparently Dow got permission to use some of his chlorine for this purpose, for in 1900 he did make and sell considerable sulfur chloride to the rubber industry. Demand fell off for a year or so and no more was made until 1902. Then sulfur chloride became a raw material for the manufacture of chloroform, and became and has been ever since an important Dow product. It was the first Dow product other than bleach to use chlorine. Today there are hundreds of such products. Some were foreseen by Herbert Dow; some were undreamed-of by him or any of his contemporaries.

At about the same time, still when he was supposed to be keeping his mind on bleach and pharmaceutical bromides, Dow and his colleagues successfully put into operation one of the first large-scale organic syntheses to be achieved in an American chemical factory. This was the synthesis of chloroform, and it was such a triumph in its day, when organic synthesis succeeded usually only in Germany, that it is worth examining in some detail here.

Up to this time, the standard way to make chloroform was to combine bleach and acetone. The acetone had usually been obtained by the destructive distillation of wood, which made it and the final product pretty expensive. Professor Smith and a colleague, Professor William O. Quayle, worked out in the laboratory at Case School a process for making chloroform without the use of expensive acetone.

They showed the process to Herbert Dow, and he was very much interested. For one thing, the chemical formula for chloroform is $CHCl_3$— meaning that each molecule of chloroform contains three atoms of the chlorine he wanted so much to find uses for. There was an increasingly large market for chloroform, owing partly to its growing use as an anesthetic in childbirth. And the proposed process, if it worked in the factory, would enable Dow to come on the chloroform market at prices below those of the users of the standard bleach-acetone process.

Thus it came about that, some twenty-five or thirty years later, Dr. Mark E. Putnam, now general manager of The Dow Chemical Company, was writing in the Silver Anniversary Volume of the American Institute of Chemical Engineers:

In the early part of the period under discussion (that is, in the early 1900's) The Dow Chemical Company, which had already achieved success in the manufacture of chlorine and bromine, turned attention to the organic field as an outlet for its products. The first attempt resulted in the manufacture of chloroform by a purely synthetic process, the raw materials being carbon in the form of charcoal, hydrogen from iron and water, and chlorine. On the face of things, an attempt to manufacture chloroform by this scheme showed evidence of remarkable faith in the theories of organic chemistry. However, as actually carried out, the process was not quite such a strain on one's chemical credulity.

Charcoal and sulfur were heated together to produce carbon bisulfide. Sulfur and chlorine were allowed to react, with the formation of sulfur chloride. Then the carbon bisulfide was treated with sulfur chloride, and carbon tetrachloride formed. The carbon tetrachloride was reduced with fine iron and water under carefully controlled conditions, and chloroform resulted. At first the carbon bisulfide was purchased from the Taylor Process Co., but as soon as the chloroform business was definitely established a plant was built for its production.

This process involved several interesting chemical engineering problems. All of its reactions required careful heat control. All were corrosive; some were violent. New types of apparatus had to be evolved. To the best of my knowledge, the large rotating tumbler with accurate heat control was first used in this plant for organic reactions on a large scale. At the cost of much work and at least one explosion, relatively safe ways of reacting carbon bisulfide and sulfur chloride were found. New columns were developed for accurately fractionating chloroform and carbon tetrachloride, both of which were too corrosive for the ordinary columns then in use. Later, carbon tetrachloride proved of much greater importance than the chloroform for which the process was originally designed.

Actually, it took several years for the process as described above to operate as it was supposed to. There were the usual hitches involved in enlarging a laboratory process to factory size. Equipment that is now commonplace had to be evolved and built, with a minimum of expenditure. And there was available in The Dow Chemical Company, or anywhere else in America, very little experience with large-scale organic synthesis.

Professor Quayle came from Case School, set up the process, and for six years had charge of it. The first Dow chloroform was sold in 1903. But the yield—that is, the proportion of finished material to the starting ingredients —remained stubbornly low and in time began to get lower. Young Dr. E. O. Barstow took charge of the operation and found that pipe joints were leaking chloroform so profusely that in fact only about half of the expected yield was obtained. He ripped out all the plumbing and put new in; within a couple of months the plant was on a paying basis. He then turned the plant over to Dr. C. J. Strosacker, under whom it went on increasing in productivity.

It was not long, by the way, before the carbon tetrachloride which was made as an intermediate in the new chloroform process became a more important Dow product than the chloroform itself, and was being sold by the millions of pounds a year. "Carbon tet" is nonflammable, and a great deal of this output went into the new wall-type fire extinguishers which were just then coming on the market. Another important use was as a solvent for fats, oils, and greases—both in factories and in nonflammable drycleaning fluids for home use. It has been ever since one of the most widely used of chlorinated organic solvents.[2]

[2] By 1916 Dow sales of "carbon tet" had risen to 11,000,000 pounds a year from the 400,000 pounds they had been in 1908. This was at the time the largest organic synthesis yet conducted in an American chemical factory.

To avoid confusing the reader, the business arrangement under which the chloroform project was achieved has not yet been mentioned. When Herbert Dow decided to put Professor Smith's proposed process to work in the factory, he apparently foresaw that the directors of The Dow Chemical Company would feel that chloroform was too far afield from bromides and bleach to justify their voting the money to set up a plant. Accordingly, in June of 1902, a small company was organized and given the name of Midland Chemical Company.[3] Practically all the stockholders and directors were already in Dow Chemical; most of the personnel and all the chlorine came from the Dow plant, just across the road. Above all, there came from across the road the spirit of enterprise and development.

SO FAR, WE HAVE SEEN Herbert Dow stretch his original assignment to make bleach and one bromide to include a full line of pharmaceutical bromides, bromide for the photographic industry, mining salts, sulfur, chloride, and chloroform. All this was achieved in a handful of years, during which he was also fighting for existence with the English bleach trust and then with the German bromine trust.

But even all this activity seems not to have convinced him that he was bursting fast enough out of his original bleach-and-one-bromide cocoon. At any rate, he and Dr. Barstow undertook, starting in 1905, the manufacture of benzoic acid. This was a task little understood outside of Germany, and in fact most of the benzoic acid used in America came from that country. Dr. Barstow's process consisted of treating toluene with chlorine, and then converting the resultant benzyl chloride into benzoic acid. The success of the process made The Dow Chemical Company one of the first suppliers of that chemical in this country.

For several years, a great deal of Dow benzoic acid was converted at the plant to benzoate of soda, a popular food preservative. Production and sales of Dow benzoate were going along nicely when the Federal Government, misled by an ill-informed journalistic campaign, suddenly banned the use of benzoate in foods. This happened in 1908. The ban came off shortly afterwards, but Dow had meanwhile shifted his emphasis in this line to benzyl chloride and benzoic acid. This early organic venture was to mean more in Dow history than its size at the time indicated. It involved

[3] Sometimes known around Midland as Midland Chemical Company II, to distinguish it from the original company of that name bought up in 1900. In 1914 this second Midland Chemical Company was incorporated into the Dow organization.

work with the so-called "benzene ring," which in general only the Germans were attempting on a factory basis. Today the benzene ring is the starting material of hundreds of complex and useful products turned out by modern chemical factories; in some of these products The Dow Chemical Company pioneered and still leads the field. Part of the company's success here may well be due to its early grass-roots experience in dealing with the benzene ring's complicated and then little-known chemistry—and above all to its early-established habit of willingness to attack any chemical problem, however difficult.

An interesting feature of this early organic venture was the primitive but effective attempt at chemical photosynthesis which worked and made the process work. It was known that the chief problem of making benzyl chloride was to get the toluene and chlorine to react, and that this could be achieved best in sunlight. In the spirit of "trying anything" with available materials, half the roof was removed from an old building and replaced with glass. Under this glass was erected a multitude of glass tubes which were filled with broken glass. Chlorine gas rose through these tubes, met toluene trickling down, and (except on cloudy days) produced benzyl chloride. Nowadays there is a whole science of photosynthesis, complete with equipment for producing "sunlight" or other forms of radiant energy twenty-four hours a day. Herbert Dow never did learn to wait around for such sciences and their proper scientific equipment to be invented—he just went on and made do with whatever ideas and equipment he and his team could muster. Not all of them worked as well as the "Barstow's Greenhouse" described above, but a lot of them did. Nor did failure, however dismal, ever keep Dow from trying again. He would pick up the pieces, if any, and presently they would be milling about as part of one or more new ideas.

Two OTHER DOW IDEAS of this cocoon-bursting period deserve mention here. One was a project for buying the cheap Saginaw Valley coal mined near Midland and "reducing" it for its chemical constituents. The "chemistry of coal," already nicely established in England and Germany, was just getting a start in this country: it was eventually to produce hundreds of dyes, medicines, fabrics, and so on. With his fondness for exploiting cheap and easily available local materials, Herbert Dow thought he saw in Saginaw Valley coal a project he could clasp to his heart. Unfortunately, this coal, though both cheap and easily available, was also quite worthless except as inexpensive boiler fuel—for which he was already using it. But he never gave up the notion of going in person, wherever feasible, to Nature's own supply of raw materials, and today The Dow Chemical Company derives millions of pounds of starting materials from petroleum brought to Midland or natural gas brought to its works in Texas. It also takes millions of pounds of bromine, chlorine and metallic magnesium out of that cheapest of all natural resources, the ocean. Herbert Dow was at work on the bromine part of this venture at the time of his death, as we shall see in Chapter 21.

Another Dow idea of this time failed so hard that it made him as financially "broke" as he had been in his earliest days. In 1904 he had written to Mr. Osborn, like a worldly son advising an inexperienced father:

Mining propositions sometimes pay an enormous profit but they are the most treacherous and uncertain investment known, and I hope you will not go into it very heavy.

Like many a giver of good advice, Herbert Dow sometimes forgot to heed his own counsel. Several years later he became a relatively heavy investor in the Ontario Nickel Company, which he hoped was going to use a lot of Dow bromine compounds to recover nickel from ore. A more economical way was discovered and the whole thing fell through. In June of 1908 he was writing a friend:

So far as I am concerned personally, the financial panic last fall and the past winter has so affected stockholders of our nickel enterprise that the burden of the thing has fallen largely on me and I have put into it every cent that I could rake or scrape, in order to get it in shape where the officers would not clear us out. It took my last dollar to such an extent that I did not even pay my tailor for clothes that I purchased before I realized in what hard shape our other Ontario Nickel stockholders were. There has never been a time since I was married when I have been under the financial strain that I am at present.

Several months after that, though, Dow was saying:

I lost a lot of money on the nickel proposition, but I brought back to Midland the only good thing they had up there—a chemist named Strosacker.

So much for Herbert Dow's early efforts to burst from the limited field in which, in the routine financial thinking of the day, the young new Dow Chemical Company belonged. Some of the efforts failed; many were, in the light of modern chemical science, characterized by main strength and awkwardness. But behind and all through them was the will, often frustrated but never stilled, to go on seeking and finding and growing.

11

THE BROMINE WAR

The dow chemical company was still breathing hard from the finan-cial squeeze of the bleach war with the English when a new "war" began. This one was with the Germans, and it involved the struggling young com-pany's other chief source of revenue—bromine.

Bromine had at that time only two important uses: in sedative medicines and in the making of photographic films. These uses called for, at most, a few hundred thousand pounds of bromine a year, usually in the form of bromides.[1]

As an exception to the usual rule, bromine and bromides appear to have been made in the United States before they were made on a commercial scale in Europe: there were several small bromine plants in Pennsylvania and in what is now West Virginia, back before the Civil War. The real bromine industry began, almost simultaneously in the United States and in Germany, around the year 1865. Bromine plants sprang up in profusion along the valley of the Ohio River, and the Germans began getting bromine as a by-product from their vast potash deposits at Stassfurt. The price had been $10.00 a pound; competition soon brought it down to $4.50. By the time Herbert Dow was testing out his proposed blowing-out process at Canton, the price in the United States was running between 30 and 40 cents. Dow got his process worked out and into production, and prices in the United States settled to between 20 and 25 cents.

At those prices, which were vehemently competitive, the Germans de-veloped no interest in the American market, where so many of their other chemicals were enjoying virtual monopolies. They chose, instead, to

---

[1] A side result of this was that the chem-Ical term "bromide" came into everyday language as a handy description of people, expressions, and things that are dull and hackneyed. Medicinal bromides are any-thing but mental stimulants, nor were the photographs taken in those days conspicu-ous for liveliness and originality.

concentrate on the German market and on the rest of the world, which they considered their own private preserve. To the orderly Teutonic mind, it made very good sense that American bromine manufacturers should devote themselves entirely to competing with one another, ruinously if possible, to supply their own country—while German manufacturers should divide up their own country and the rest of the world, keep everyone else out, and sell bromides for whatever they all agreed to charge. In fact, to do just that the German manufacturers were united into a cartel called Die Deutsche Bromkonvention—"convention" being used in its diplomatic sense of "arrangement" or "understanding." The job of this outfit was to parcel out markets among its members, set the prices to be charged, and keep an eye out for intruders.

Everything was going along smoothly until Herbert Dow decided to sell some bromides in Europe.

Then the fireworks began.

As far as money was concerned, bromine was not a very important German product. The whole Konvention seldom produced more than a million pounds in a year. Even at monopoly prices, this brought in only a couple of hundred thousand dollars of profit, which had to be divided among about thirty companies. But it was the old story of "it isn't the money; it's the principle of the thing." This "principle" was that the world chemical market belonged to the German chemical industry. Intruders were not to be tolerated, even on such relatively minor matters as bromides.

With Herbert Dow, it was a question both of principle *and* of money. Submissiveness was not one of his character traits: he felt entitled to sell his bromides to whoever would buy them, regardless of who might or might not like it. Besides, with the effects of the bleach war still being felt, he needed money and needed it desperately.

We know by a letter to him from Mr. Osborn that as early as 1896 Herbert Dow had proposed to sell abroad some of the bromides the Midland Chemical Company was making. This proposal very much upset Mr. Osborn, and he wrote out at some length and fervor the reasons why it upset him. The chief of these was, frankly, that the Germans certainly would not like it and would manifest their displeasure by flooding the American market with cut-price bromides. That tactic, he pointed out, was standard practice with German chemical manufacturers in such cases, and would almost surely put Dow and the other American bromide manufacturers out of business. Should Dow dare to export, Mr. Osborn predicted:

. . . the Germans would retaliate by dumping hundreds of tons of surplus stock on us. I have no idea whatever that they would surrender any part of their market without a bitter fight. We would be the aggressors. They have unlimited means and want more market as well as ourselves, and the fight would likely be to the death.

Seen one way, this advice does not look very courageous: it resembles the warnings given by hack politicians to an earnest candidate who wants to take a stand on an issue. On the other hand, Mr. Osborn's advice had, in its time and place, a very practical wisdom. In 1896, Herbert Dow and the Midland Chemical Company were as yet none too definitely established in the domestic market. Might they not be wise to get on a firm footing there, before stirring up trouble from abroad?

No record exists of Herbert Dow's reaction to these arguments. By that time he was no longer general manager of the Midland Chemical Company; nor was he to regain control of his bromine process till the new Dow Chemical Company bought out the Midland Chemical Company and its bromine facilities in 1900. But it was never Herbert Dow's practice to surrender an idea of which he thought highly: about the only concession he would ever make was to store it away in the back of his head for future consideration. This particular idea of selling bromides abroad stayed in storage a full seven years, which was not a long time for a notion of Dow's.

Then, late in 1903, he shipped some of his bromides to England and put them on the market. His price was well under that set by the Bromkonvention, which charged English consumers what it chose for bromine, they having no source of supply of their own. Years later, Dow described the German reaction:

> Herr Jacobson, of the Deutsche Bromkonvention, came to Midland and told me that he had positive evidence that we had exported Bromides. I said, "What of it?" He said, "Don't you know that you can't export Bromides?" I said, "I know nothing of the kind." He replied that he was sent here by the Deutsche Bromkonvention to tell me that for every pound of Bromide we sent out of the United States, they would put two in, and that price had nothing to do with it. I thought he was bluffing and paid no attention to him.

For over a year Dow went on exporting bromides to Europe and elsewhere, in greater and greater amounts, nor was any word heard from the Konvention. Then, suddenly and without explanation, a bank in New York which held some demand notes on The Dow Chemical Company sent notice that these notes were to be paid immediately. The company was having a rough financial time from the bleach war, and this request was not very pleasant; nor did anybody in Midland know what had brought it about. Three or four days later, however, all became clear. German bromides had just come on the American market at 15 cents—about half the price Dow had been charging.

Then, a few days after that, a strange telegram came from New York. Herr Jacobson had just arrived from Bromkonvention headquarters in Germany, was very much out of sorts, and wanted Dow to report to him in New York at once. This peremptory summons overtook Dow in St. Louis, where Mr. and Mrs. Dow and the children were changing trains on their way to a vacation in California.

Dow was the type of man who would not have reported to New York or anywhere else to meet all the crowned heads of Europe, let alone a Herr Jacobson. However, wires began coming in from worried customers, pleading that he at least see the man. Dow finally agreed to wait over a day in St. Louis, in case Herr Jacobson cared to overtake him there. Herr Jacobson came, and here is Dow's account of their meeting:

I had a meeting in St. Louis with Herr Jacobson at his request, just after he made the first spectacular cut, and he stated that the goods were sent in here to punish us for exporting Bromides. I would not agree *not* to export Bromides, and the conference was broken up. The whole situation is very spectacular and intended to frighten us.

Jacobson insisted on further parley, but Dow went on to California. Meanwhile, President Convers was writing to Dow:

My idea is that we ought to ship Bromide to Germany in such quantities as to completely upset the market there if it is possible to do so. . . . It seems as though the only way to bring Jacobson to terms will be to demoralize his market if possible at the point where he is getting his profit.

This idea of dumping bromine right back in the Konvention's home market was adopted and became the nub of Dow's strategy in the fight, which lasted nearly four years. It is not hard to see what made the tactic effective. When a German chemical cartel set out to crush an upstart like Dow by price-cutting, *it invariably cut prices only in the proposed victim's market, but kept prices on a monopoly basis at home and everywhere else.* In this way, a relatively small portion of the monopoly's profits could be told off to quell minor sporadic resistance, much as the general of a large army might send a regiment or two of soldiers to put down a local disturbance. But Dow's resistance was neither minor nor sporadic, nor did he bother to come to grips with the regiment or two sent to bring him to terms. Instead, he went after the army itself, right on its home grounds. In short, for several years Dow practically ignored his own domestic bromine market, and concentrated instead on selling in Germany and the Konvention's next most profitable bailiwick, England; and in both those countries he was able to sell at well under the Konvention's artificially high prices.[2] Here is Herbert Dow's own "dispatch from the front" on the contest, contained in a letter to Cady Staley, president of Case School and a stockholder:

When this 15-cent price was made over here, instead of meeting it, we pulled out of the American market altogether and used all our production to supply the foreign demand. This, as we afterward learned, was not what they anticipated we would do. Their American agent, when he accepted an agreement with the Germans to act as their distributing agent on this side, was told that it was only a temporary arrangement—a flash in the pan—and that it would soon all be over.

Later the German producers got into trouble among themselves as to who was to supply the goods for the American market and the American agent became embarrassed by reason of his inability to get goods that he had contracted to supply and asked us if we would take his contracts. This, of course, we refused to do.

In the meantime, we had effected quite an organization abroad and had got some very good agents, especially our representatives in London and Hamburg. We, however, required a great deal more working capital to handle this business than was necessary when we sold granular Bromides to the Americans on a strictly ten-day basis. All our Bromides that have been sent to Europe have been consigned and we now have something like $20,000 worth in Germany alone or in transit there.

Both our Mt. Pleasant [3] and Midland Bromide plants are running full and our Bromide is always sold at a profit and we have reason to think that our competitors in Germany have lost considerable money during this fight. In the meantime all other producers of Bromine in this country have shut down and we are therefore in a much stronger position than we ever were before, by reason of the Germans

---

[2] To this performance he later added a touch of grim humor. In its mounting anxiety to crush him, the Konvention finally began selling bromides in America at 10 cents a pound—barely enough to cover import duty and freight. Dow bought up some of these 10-cent bromides, repackaged them, and sold them in Germany at a nice profit. The Germans finally caught on to this.

[3] At Mt. Pleasant, thirty miles from Midland, Dow had brine wells which were operated during times of large demand for bromine. Crude bromides were made there and shipped to Midland for processing and "packaging."

having respect for us, which is a very hard thing to obtain, for the reason they cannot conceive that it is possible for anyone outside of Germany to compete with them in the manufacture of any chemical. In most lines, they are undoubtedly invincible and it is hard for them to realize that this does not apply to all lines.

It is only fair to point out, however, that Dow's "report from the front" contained more than a little whistling in the dark. As hinted in its third paragraph, his campaign was much hampered by shortage of working capital—a handicap brought about by the rigors of the bleach war. Nor were there, for the first and last time in The Dow Chemical Company's history, any dividends. Dr. Edwin O. Barstow, who along with Earl W. Bennett and other old-timers stood with Dow through the fight, said later of this period:

Dr. Herbert Dow was a man who could not be licked. During the days of the bromine war with the Germans, he always drove an old one-horse buggy which was badly in need of paint, and it needed it worse as time went on, but there was not any money. Dividends were suspended for a while. Herbert Dow stuck to it and beat the Germans at their own game.

The attack on Dow by the Germans began tapering off in 1908. By that time it was dawning on them that measures they meant to be murderous were in fact suicidal. Or they may have read in the *Berliner Tageblatt:*

The Bromkonvention has in contrast to last year suffered a remarkable loss. While in the third quarter of 1906 the sale of pure Brom amounted to 686,413 Kg., the sale of Brom in the same period of this year amounted to only 553,580 Kg. . . . Brom manufacture, in former days highly profitable, is reduced to nothing.

By 1909, the Germans had pretty much withdrawn from the American bromine market. The price of bromides here returned to the cost of manufacture plus a reasonable profit, which was all that Herbert Dow had ever wanted. Dow came back into the domestic market—and also went on exporting to wherever he chose. How much it had cost the Bromkonvention to try to force him into line cannot be known, nor should anyone feel obliged to sympathize about it. A full-dress attempt to "punish" a native American industry had itself been punished, and that was all that mattered.

Years later, Dow mentioned what he thought had been the flaw in the German technique, aside from the obvious blunder of thinking that any business can maintain itself indefinitely by bluff. The flaw has probably already occurred to the reader: instead of practically giving their bromides away here, the Konvention would have been wise to take a cent or two profit on each pound. That way, Dow pointed out, they could have kept the pressure on him indefinitely, instead of having eventually to give up—and swallow a loss in money and prestige into the bargain.

Incidentally, the Germans never lost their hard-earned respect for Herbert Dow as a fighter. In the last years of his life, they toyed with the notion of producing metallic magnesium (at which they were very good) in this country. They knew metallic magnesium was a special pet of Herbert Dow's, and that he had been going through years of frustration trying to get a business in it established. Rumors of their proposed arrival, they hoped, might make him consider withdrawing from the field. But he refused to withdraw, and the Germans did not come. In this they resembled Mark Twain's celebrated cat: having once sat down on a hot stove, they could not persuade themselves to sit down on what they were pretty sure was a cold stove.

Dow group at office door, about 1902. Left to right are Dow, E. O. Cross, F. N. Lowry, A. C. Convers, J. E. LeFevre, J. C. Graves, D. Richardson, E. W. Bennett, T. Griswold, Jr., and M. B. Johnson. Mr. Convers was president. Mr. Bennett, then a bookkeeper, is chairman of the board of directors; Mr. Griswold is still active as a consultant on engineering matters.

Dow plant in 1902. In the foreground is the "Old Mill," where many a Dow process was to be developed. In the background, between the brine-well derrick and the powerhouse chimneys, stands the apparatus by which Dow was trying to reduce Saginaw Valley coal to tar, gas, and ammonia. Always creative and overflowing with ideas, Dow was often ahead of his time.

Carbon tetrachloride in action. One of Dow's first volume products other than bromides and bleach was "carbon tet." It soon found wide use in the type of fire extinguisher here being demonstrated. Millions of pounds of it still go to this use. (Photo by courtesy of Pyrene Manufacturing Company.)

12

AT THE THRESHOLD OF TODAY'S CHEMISTRY

WE NOTED IN CHAPTER TEN HERBERT DOW'S UNWILLINGNESS TO REMAIN JUST A bleach and bromides manufacturer, and the additional products by which he hoped to break the company out of that cocoon. Fortunately, these products turned out, almost from the start, to be good though not startling bread-and-butter items. The mining salts sold well, and so did the sulfur chloride, chloroform, benzyl chloride, and benzoic acid. By 1910, carbon tetrachloride production was up to one hundred thousand pounds a month. Lime sulfur and lead arsenate, both insecticides, were added to the company's list in 1910, and also did fairly well.

It was very fortunate indeed that these items succeeded and brought in some money, for both the bromine and bleach wars had been Pyrrhic victories. Pyrrhus, the reader recalls, was the ancient general who handed the Romans a beating but lost most of his army in the process and glumly remarked, "One more such victory over the Romans, and we are utterly undone." Herbert Dow may or may not have been thinking of Pyrrhus when he observed later: "It's a good thing the bleach and bromine fights didn't both come at the same time." It was also, as already noted, a good thing that other items than bleach and bromine were bringing in income.[1]

Against this background, and starting in earnest the same year that the bromine war ended, Herbert Dow began a search for some more new products. This was in 1909, and by July of that year he had this reaction from Professor Smith of Case:

[1] Actually, production and sale of bromides and bleach *increased* during the "wars," but the profit on them dwindled to little or nothing. Even so, 1909 was the only year in the company's history when no dividends were paid, though they did remain very small for a year or two afterwards. Employee profit-sharing was out between 1903 and 1913, but was in force all the other years between 1900 and 1930. This was one of the first employee profit-sharing arrangements in American industry, and Herbert Dow waged some brisk battles in its defense.

I am extremely anxious, for all of us who have our whole means in the Dow stock, that the company should make a fair return during the next five or ten years, rather than begin ten or twenty years hence. Whether we beat the world or not is a secondary matter. It seems to me that you have, like our mayor of Cleveland, fought so long, that you are obliged to continue when there is no real need, solely from habit.

And not long after that, President Convers turned over to Dow, presumably with a thin smile, this letter from an upset stockholder:

When I learn of Mr. Dow's buying apparatus costing thousands of dollars just to try once and throw aside, I wonder where his conscience is. Allowing a margin for exaggeration I have reason to think Mr. Dow is better fitted for a laboratory than as Superintendent. Had he some rich patron of science who had plenty of money to expend in investigation 'twould be a worthy use to put it to. Mr. Dow no doubt has a gift of discovery. He is an enthusiast along that line, but not a safe man to expend the money of poor widows and orphans.[2]

What was Herbert Dow doing this time that could upset even Professor Smith, who had so long been such a loyal fellow crusader for progress? The answer is simple. In his first wave of advance beyond bromides and bleach, he had chosen to add to his line products that were already known and understood, and for which there was already a market. People knew what mining salts were and what they were used for; the same went for chloroform and sulfur chloride and so on. *But now he was spending time and whatever money he could get in order to look for products which did not yet exist, or which were known to exist but to have no immediate commercial use.* In short, he was doing, as early as 1909, what few other American industrial chemists were yet daring to do—but which all of them do now as a matter of course. He was making the chemical factory a *creative* place—*a place where new products useful to people are thought up and made.*

The Germans had been at this sort of thing for some time. Their organic chemical industry, though small and elementary by today's standards, had

---

[2] Those were the days in which if a business enterprise made money, it was grinding the faces of the poor; if it did not make money, it was bilking poor widows and orphans. Originally, poor widows and orphans owned just the railroads, but soon they were turning up wherever a dividend was missed. At the time the above letters were written, Herbert Dow could not pay the tailor for the suit of clothes he was coming to work in.

been active for decades. Their research chemists were already accepted as very important people, and above all as *useful* people.[3] These men had already contrived to synthesize some dyes, medicinals and other organic products found in nature, and a few that are not. Thus they had already begun the chemical industry's march into the limitless area of pure *creation*— the area in which nowadays are produced so many new dyes, medicines, vitamins, hormones, lubricants, solvents, finishes, plastics, fabrics, and other things useful and desirable in everyday life. It was in this area—of which the limitlessness was as yet not even dimly suspected—that Herbert Dow now proposed to invest some company time, effort, and dollars. He wanted to research proposed products that might or might not allow themselves to be brought into existence, and might never pay for themselves if they were.

It is not hard to see how this let's-explore-and-see-what-we-can-find attitude, coming at the depths of the attrition from the bleach and bromine wars, gave rise to concern. At the very moment when his company could least afford it, Herbert Dow seemed to be chasing chimeras instead of chemicals.

One of the chimeras which he chose to chase at this time was synthetic rubber. That was in 1909, a good thirty years before American manufacturers were to get anywhere with this difficult product. This early attempt of Dow's was conducted at Midland and produced a dozen or so gummy substances, all of which lost any resemblance they might have had to rubber after standing a few days in the air. As the reader is by now aware, such disappointments had about the same effect on Herbert Dow as water on a duck's back. By 1913 he was at work on rubber again, this time through Dr. Mark E. Putnam, a young professor at Case School. Dr. Putnam did make some synthetic rubber, but like many another "synthetic rubber" made in this country in the next twenty-five years or so, it gave little promise as either a rubber or as a commercial venture. However, the project was indirectly beneficial, as it helped eventually to bring Dr. Putnam to Midland.[4]

[3] American business and industry were still not quite over their traditional fear that the academically trained mind is necessarily impractical. Dow never shared this curious nervousness. He communed freely with doctors of philosophy and professors, and many of both that he hired are today high in the company. He was himself twice made an honorary doctor for his contributions to scientific knowledge, and Dow employees have been similarly honored.

[4] The Dow Chemical Company had a very important hand in the tremendous production of synthetic rubber in this country during World War II. This was

Another pioneer interest of Herbert Dow's at this time was the so-called "cracking" of petroleum. This was another chemical feat which did not really come into its own in the United States till many years later. Herbert Dow was very much interested in the subject as early as 1911, when he was writing to Dr. Smith:

We have been quoted 3¼ cents per gallon on the oil that distills next following kerosene, and I presume an even lower price could be secured.

If this were cracked by passing over hot bricks, it would—as I understand it—make a mixture of benzol, toluol, methane, ethylene, light paraffin oils, etc.

By October of 1913, Herbert Dow was far beyond the idea stage in his gasoline cracking, and was reporting to Dr. Smith:

The gas that we make by cracking gasoline contains quite a percentage of butadiene. . . .

And a week or so later Dow wrote to Dr. Smith:

We have succeeded in making ethylene dibromide in a very satisfactory way by cracking pentane. . . .

These bits of information make pretty clear what Dow was actually after. He was looking for a cheap and plentiful source for such unsaturated hydrocarbons as butadiene and ethylene, which he knew could be treated with chemicals like chlorine to make almost an infinitude of new compounds. This was one of the things the Germans had already begun to do and which Herbert Dow very much wanted to do. Considering the little that was then really known of these hydrocarbons, the fact that few commercially useful products from them were yet in sight, and the precarious state of the company's finances, it is probably just as well that Herbert Dow was not too communicative to his directors about this interest of his. They would have been as little delighted if he had told them he was now putting company time and money into astronomy.

Actually, what Dow was up to was the thing he never had and never would stop doing: he was looking for new uses for his bromine and chlorine. These two elements he already had in abundance. He had tried combining

because the company was at that time the country's only producer of styrene, and, until the very eve of the war, the country's only producer of butadiene. Most of the rubber made during the war was produced by combining butadiene with styrene. The Dow Company produced millions of tons of styrene itself and showed other companies how to produce it. Today styrene is the basis of several important plastics, including Dow's Styron. That is just one of its uses.

Sept 1909

Rubber substitutes made with castor oil, S_2Br_2 or S_2Cl_2 and CS_2.

CS_2 used as a solvent to diminish the violence of the reaction.

oil	S_2Br_2	S_2Cl_2	CS_2	Remarks	Color
80	6		25	Hard, brittle, too much S_2Br_2	Brown
30	4½		25	Fair Substitute.	brown
30	3		25	Would not congeal	brown
30	4		10	Reaction too violent, thick, porous	
30	4		25	Fair Substitute, sticky	brown
30	4		20	" "	brown
30	4		10	" "	brown
80		4	10	" " Violent reaction	white
30		3½	10	Would not congeal. White	
30		4½	15	Fair Substitute	White
30		4	20	" spongy	White
80		4	5	Spongy	white
30		4	25		White

These substitutes altho good at first after standing in a warm room for a few days become very soft and sticky.

Pioneering in synthetic rubber. Here is a "lab report" on a 1909 attempt by Dow to do something that was not really accomplished in this country till some thirty years later. Early results, as the glum comment at the end indicates, were not very encouraging.

them with every other chemical he could be sure of obtaining in quantity and economically. Now it was the turn of the unsaturated hydrocarbons, and he wanted to be sure of getting them cheaply in case he turned something up. This eagerness to beat the bushes to see what sort of game ran out is illustrated by a letter Dow wrote in 1909 to Professor E. W. Morley, a stockholder who was a famous physicist:

We think there is a royal road to fortune for The Dow Chemical Company but the exact location of the road is enveloped in a fog. We have no doubt that you can be of some assistance to us and are, therefore, writing you very fully.

If a new use for Bromine could be found and The Dow Co. got nothing out of it directly, the increased market for Bromine would still be of enormous value to the Dow Company. Suppose a new use developed that took one million pounds of some easily-made Bromide per year . . . .

No record exists of Dr. Morley's reaction to the million-pounds-a-year figure, which must have struck him as preposterously large. The fact is, however, that before Herbert Dow's death twenty-one years later, the company was well on the way to using over a million pounds of bromine a *month* in one product alone: ethylene dibromide, used in antiknock gasolines. Today the company needs so much bromine for this one chemical that it has to go to the ocean to get it. Incidentally, ethylene dibromide was just one of the dozens of compounds which Dow worked up at this time by treating unsaturated hydrocarbons with bromine or chlorine. Nor was it the only one which was to pay off decades later.[5]

Herbert Dow wrote and talked so much about bromine at this time that his colleagues came to look on it as a sort of underprivileged child which he was determined should have a place in life. When he asked Dr. Putnam to work on the synthesis of rubber, his one instruction was that every effort be made to use bromine as a starting material. A few years before, in setting

[5] Chemists may be curious to know exactly what these compounds were. A report which Dr. Strosacker laid on Herbert Dow's desk early in 1914 listed about twenty, including perchlorethylene, acetylene tetrabromide, trichloro ethylene, hexachlorethane, and vinylidiene chloride. Other work done at this same time by Herbert Dow and his associates included making a complex series of acetates and formates to be tested as possible solvents for cellulose acetate and cellulose nitrate. Knowing of today's huge market for "vinyl plastics" and the importance of vinyl chloride in making plastics like Saran, many a chemist will smile at the following note from Dow to Smith, showing how hard they were working at Midland *not to make* vinyl chloride:

"We are finding it very difficult to make monochlormethyl acetate. With potash we make glycol diacetate and both potassium bromide and chloride. With zinc acetate no zinc chloride is made, but there is a great tendency to make vinyl chloride. We are now attempting to prevent the formation of vinyl chloride by carrying on the reaction in the presence of hydrobromic acid, whereby vinyl chloride as fast as made will be converted into monochlormonobromethane."

Dr. C. J. Strosacker to work on an early attempt to synthesize indigo, he had issued the same order. In fact, veteran Dow chemists recall that for years they could not start work on a new product or process without being told, "Be sure to try bromine." There were three reasons for this. One was of course that Dow had a lot of bromine. Another was that Herbert Dow never could see a lot of anything lying around, especially where he could get at it, without feeling an overpowering need to find some use for it. Finally, he never could bear to accept as final the idea that all possible uses for a chemical had already been found. As he wrote in 1909 to Professor Burgess at the University of Wisconsin:

> We have just been looking over the statistics and unless we are mistaken, there is no elementary substance that sells for as little money as bromine but that is worth very much more per pound. This would seem to indicate that the development in its manufacture has been far greater than the development in its uses. While this reasoning does not prove that there is a big field to develop in the application of bromine, yet it proves that there is either a field of this kind, or that bromine has a smaller use in the arts than any other known element. It may be that elementary chemistry has so impressed the idea upon all chemists that bromine is like chlorine—only less so—that the peculiar properties of bromine have been overlooked or ignored.

Connoisseurs of pure logic will have to decide for themselves whether this syllogism of Herbert Dow's stands up or not. He would have been the last one to care. All he was trying to convey was that *he* was sure there were undiscovered uses for bromine, and he was going to find them. It was the same with chlorine, with the hydrocarbons, with every other chemical he knew he could get his hands on cheaply and in quantity.

Naturally, Herbert Dow was by no means the *only* American chemical manufacturer thinking along these lines back in 1909. But he was one of the very first, and it is due in great part to the exploring spirit of men like him that the chemical industry is today so directly and intimately useful in people's everyday lives. Actually, these men stood, back at a time when such a stand was not popular with stockholders and boards of directors, for *research*. Nowadays no chemical company would seriously expect to grow in usefulness unless it spent a great deal of time, brains, and money ceaselessly searching for new products or ways to improve established ones.

It would be pleasant to report that these speculative explorations by Dow turned up at least a few things of immediate, specific value. They did not. They did, though, accomplish things that were eventually to prove far more productive. They inculcated in the men around Herbert Dow his own un-yielding spirit of always seeking to do new things and do the old ones better. They laid a groundwork of knowledge and *confidence* which, when the chance at last came for American manufacturers to stand up to and finally surpass the German organic chemical industry, enabled The Dow Chemical Company to accomplish its full share in that useful achievement. In a word, they helped make the company the persistently *creative* organization it is today.

In the light of all this, the reader may be a bit amused by the following exchange of letters. Dow had gone to great pains to set up, at a chemical exposition held in 1916, a display of the chemicals his searches had turned up. His hope, of course, was to receive some nibbles from industry that would justify putting at least some of these chemicals into production. He got exactly one nibble, as follows:

DEAR SIR: As a teacher of Organic Chemistry, I was greatly interested in your display of halogenated derivatives of ethane and methane, at the recent Chemical Exposition. The series of mixed bromine and chlorine derivatives on display offered such unusual opportunities for teaching the possibilities of structure chemistry, that I would be glad to learn your prices for small samples of these compounds, with a view to adding them to our museum specimens.

The "possibilities of structure chemistry" were where Herbert Dow rightly foresaw that much of the future of the chemical industry and of his company lay. It must have given him quite a twinge to find that their only invitation was to a museum; it must have been as disconcerting as taking a harp to a party and not being asked to play on it. Nevertheless he wrote back courteously:

We do not carry the unusual halogen compounds of ethane and methane in stock, but have worked up a commercial process for the manufacture of every one of them. Occasionally we get an order for some of them, and I will put your name on our list and will endeavor to send you samples occasionally as we make up these new and unusual compounds, for which there will be no charge.

Today some of these "new and unusual compounds" leave the Dow plants by the trainload. Some of them have long since given rise to other new and unusual compounds which also go out by the trainload. And more are in sight. The spirit of Herbert Dow is no more ready for a museum now than it was in 1916.

13

$2NaCl + 2H_2O + ELECTRICITY =$
$2NaOH + Cl_2 + H_2$

It was around 1908, just when he was trying to see to and over the expanding chemical horizon, that Herbert Dow began to become actively discontented with his chlorine cells. This was indeed news around the plant, for these were the cells he himself had developed as a youth and as a very young man, and on which the very being of The Dow Chemical Company was based.

Though crude to the eye, having been built in the shop of the cheapest possible materials, Dow's cells had made him a figure in industrial chemistry. His bromine cells produced more bromine, more economically, than any other American plant. Nor were the homemade chlorine cells far behind them in efficiency—at least for a time. Together the two kinds of cell had kept the company going through repeated financial panics, and had enabled it to stand up against the powerful onslaughts of the English bleach and German bromide combines.

But now, Dow began to see, the usefulness of his chlorine cells was drawing to a close. Their handicap was that they produced only chlorine. Other chlorine manufacturers' cells produced at least one additional product, generally sodium hydroxide, otherwise known as caustic soda.[1] This caustic soda, sold in great quantity to the soap, glass, and other industries, provided an important source of income—and so made the chlorine produced along with it a great deal cheaper than if it had been produced alone.

It is true that the Dow cells did have, in a way, a second product along with the chlorine. This was, of course, the bromine which was taken out of the brine before the chlorine was. But the bromine did not sell in large enough quantities to balance the fact that the chlorine cells themselves

---

[1] Also known as lye. Originally lye was the liquor got from dissolving wood ashes in water. Today lye is any strong alkali—particularly caustic soda.

Dow's philosophy of building, as of 1898. Dow built his early plants mostly of cheap wood partly because he had to and partly for other reasons. Here is the start of a brief essay on the subject in one of his notebooks. The original text reads:

"We will consider two systems of conducting a chemical manufactory.

"The 1st—The European method is to have all apparatus as durable as possible unless extreme expense prohibits.

"The 2nd—Our method that we carry to an extreme is to have all apparatus as cheap as possible and as accessible for inspection and repairs as possible.

"Nothing is as cheap or as readily repaired as wooden apparatus.

"If the first cost of this apparatus is one fifth of other apparatus and its life one fifth, we get the same profit from one fifth the investment and consequently five times the dividend on the investment that we would have done had we adopted the European durable apparatus policy al-though cost of production may be no less in one case than the other.

"By our method we run risks of leakages of both gas and liquids that may be very serious.

"This should be guarded against by special apparatus, special chemical tests at frequent intervals and special bookkeeping to see that consumption of raw material and output always bear the most favorable relation to each other possible.

"These exacting requirements are somewhat of an objection but it is more than offset by the ability to modify the apparatus so as to take advantage of every improvement as soon as it is fully developed and demonstrated to have value...."

were producing only chlorine. It was, Dow saw, only a matter of time when it would be cheaper for him to buy chlorine from other manufacturers— a prospect which did not delight him.

There was another aspect of his chlorine cells which greatly displeased him. They required him to throw out as mud or sludge important quantities of sodium, calcium, and magnesium. These elements were, to be sure, not in their pure state: they were combined in one way or another with hydrogen, oxygen and/or chlorine—which, of course, got thrown out with them.

It was that wasteful situation which Herbert Dow now determined to do something about. He had to, to stay in the chlorine business. Waste was against his nature anyway. Besides, Herbert Dow knew that the only way to continue to make money in the increasingly competitive chemical industry was to do what the hog butchers were learning to do, which was to sell everything of the hog but his squeal. In terms of Dow's brines, this meant he must extract and market every chemical in them that it was economically feasible to apprehend and sell.

Herbert Dow launched his project in a curiously roundabout way. As an aftermath of the bleach and bromine wars, the company was not paying dividends at the moment; to ask his directors for enough money to research a new cell would have evoked outraged bellows. He therefore asked for what he hoped was one-third enough money, which he got and put for The Dow Chemical Company into a new little company christened the Midland Manufacturing Company. The other two thirds were put up, in equal parts, by the Fostoria Glass Company and the Libbey Glass Company.

The purpose of the new little company, in which the work was to be done by Dow chemists, was to devise an electrolytic potash cell. At this time practically all the world's potash came from the Stassfurt deposits in Germany. Glass manufacturers needed potash in very pure form: they had to buy it as potassium carbonate (K_2CO_3) and pay whatever the Germans chose to charge for it. Dow was in the same boat in buying potash for his potassium bromide.

But not all potash, even from Germany, was expensive. Potash used as an agricultural fertilizer does not have to be pure, and the Germans were shipping here boatloads of cheap KCl or potassium chloride. Herbert Dow noted this, and it gave him two bright ideas. In both the expensive potassium carbonate and the cheap potassium chloride, the important element was the potassium. Why not, he figured, develop an electrolytic cell to get potassium from the cheap potash? Then he and the two glass companies would save themselves some money—and perhaps make additional money by selling their excess potash to others.

The two glass companies "bought" this idea—and also a second which Herbert Dow tacked on as a sort of rider. Potassium and sodium are much alike chemically. A cell which would handle potassium would also be likely to handle sodium. The caustic soda that Dow wanted to make is sodium hydroxide, NaOH. In devising a potash cell he would therefore probably be devising at the same time a caustic soda cell. If this proved to be true, he would have the use of the cell in his plant to make caustic.

This was an arrangement in which all three parties stood to win and no one to lose. Each company would get potassium cheaper; the Dow Company, in return for the fact that its chemists were actually creating the cell, would have the use of it also to obtain sodium.

Research continued on a co-operative basis from 1908 to 1911, during which the proposed cell went through many versions. Some potash was made, but not much. The two glass companies became discouraged and dropped out, leaving the Dow group to go on alone. It was still some time before a really satisfactory chlorine-caustic cell was devised. The cells were introduced into the plant a few at a time, and countless improvements were made almost from month to month. Soon, as we shall presently see, the new cell and the plant processes built around it were representing the basic activity of the entire Dow Chemical Company. That is true today of the cell's various descendants. The idea then, as now, was to get every feasible penny's worth of chemicals out of the raw materials; and many chemists in and out of the company consider the founding of this new cell system to be the masterpiece of Herbert Dow's career. He himself attributed most of the new system's success to Louis E. Ward, a young electrochemist who worked on these early cells, and helped carry them forward to their present status of electrochemical achievement.[2]

Because of its immediate and future importance, it is worth while to examine here just how the new system worked. A good way to begin is to take a brief look at the system it had just replaced. The starting material, brine, was pumped from the wells to the bromine cells, where just the right current of electricity was used to liberate the bromine into the solution.

[2] Mr. Ward retired in 1950, widely recognized as one of the chief figures in this country's electrochemical industry which Dow and his associates helped pioneer and develop.

The brine with the bromine now free in it trickled down through the blowing-out tower, where upward currents of air literally blew the bromine out of the liquid. This debrominated liquid was caught and sent on to the chlorine cells, where just the right electric current caused much of the chlorine to gather at the multitudinous anodes and come off as gas. Hydrogen assembled at the cathodes and was lost. Left behind in the bottom of the cells was a sort of liquid mud consisting largely of water and some calcium, sodium, and magnesium compounds. This "mud" was periodically flushed from the cells and sent off down the sewer.

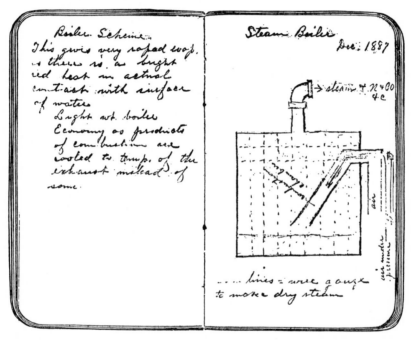

Idea for steam boiler. Dow was just twenty-one when he proposed utilizing two then new thermodynamic techniques. One was premixing fuel oil and air under pressure; the other was "direct firing" by taking the flame right to the water. All his life Dow sought ways to produce and use heat and power more efficiently.

The new cell system reintroduced into the handling of the brine the very technique—though now much refined—that Herbert Dow had invented his original bromine cells to avoid: evaporation. The reader will perhaps recall the standard method of bromine recovery at the time Herbert Dow entered the picture some twenty years before. Brine was heated in huge kettles until the salt in it formed a cake and could be removed. An oxidizing agent and an acid (usually sulfuric, because cheapest) were added to the mother liquor which remained, and this freed the bromine into the solution. The solution was then heated some more till the bromine came off as gas. Crude as this system was, it had been commercially feasible because waste wood from near-by sawmills and lumber camps provided cheap and plentiful fuel.

Dow had come into the bromine business resolved to take advantage of this cheap fuel, but in terms of inexpensive electric current to pass through the brine with no evaporation involved. Now, however, evaporation made a massive debut in the Dow plant in the form of huge vacuum evaporators heated by exhaust steam from the powerhouse engines. This was steam that had done its original job of turning the electric generators, but still contained too much heat (about 150°F.) to be thrown away quite cheerfully. This steam, routed to a series of the vacuum evaporators mentioned above, performed in ways now to be described.

The brine still came, as it always had, from the bromine plant, where it had been stripped of its bromine by electrolysis and blowing-out. Instead of going on to electrolytic chlorine cells, however, it now entered the first of the series of vacuum evaporators. These were big enclosed vacuum vats in which the liquid was successively concentrated or "shrunk" by boiling.[3] As the solution became "smaller" and "smaller," there was less and less room in it for the dissolved chemicals it contained, and they were forced out of the solution as solids. The first shrinkage in volume, taking place in the first battery of evaporators, forced out sodium chloride (common salt) which sank to the bottom and was removed. The remaining mother liquor then passed on to a second battery of evaporators, where further boiling forced out magnesium chloride. In the third and last set of evaporators, the mother liquor gave up its calcium chloride.

This meant that the brine brought from underground was now producing, besides chlorine and bromine, three additional chemicals to exploit: sodium chloride, magnesium chloride, and calcium chloride. Under the old system the brine had produced only two altogether: bromine and chlorine.

Now let's examine what happened to the new trio of chemicals thus made available.

---

[3] Which the exhaust steam was still hot enough to cause, because the vacuum lowered the boiling point. Adept use of such laws of thermodynamics—the science of exploiting the energy in fuel—figured in the success of many a Dow process.

The salt was redissolved in water and fed into the new cells we have been talking about. Here this reaction took place:

$$2NaCl + 2H_2O + \text{electricity} = 2NaOH + Cl_2 + H_2$$

In other words, salt plus water plus electricity made caustic soda plus chlorine plus hydrogen. Up to 1928, the hydrogen was allowed and even encouraged to escape into the air; after 1928 it was captured and combined with nitrogen from the air to make ammonia. Meanwhile, from the start, two usable products were coming off the cells: chlorine *and* caustic soda. This was what Herbert Dow had tried to accomplish twenty years before at Navarre, working with bought salt. Now he was working with salt derived as just *one* of his products from brine. The new cells went into volume use early in 1914, and their descendants still supply The Dow Chemical Company, month in and month out, with millions of pounds of raw materials.[4]

There was of course nothing remarkable about Dow's getting chlorine and caustic from salt and water; other chemical companies had been doing it for a decade or more. As a matter of cold fact, he was forced to do it whether he wanted to or not: his competitors had caught up with him. For all the welter of chemical ideas he lived in, Herbert Dow never for a minute overlooked the realities of industrial competition. In January of 1913, in "selling" his program of development to the directors, he wrote:

If in the future we continue to operate our plant as it is without making any changes, a part of our expenses could be cut off and our earnings for a while would increase, but later they would decrease and ultimately we would be out of business, by reason of all our plants becoming more or less antiquated, in which case

[4] There is a vein of pure rock salt almost a mile under Midland. Since 1945 this vein, tapped by water pumped down to it and then up again, has been supplying the chlorine-caustic cells at the Midland plant. This leaves the brine free to be exploited exclusively for other chemicals. Some Dow chlorine and caustic also now come out of the ocean, as do much of the company's bromine and all its metallic magnesium. Herbert Dow led this "march to the sea" in the closing years of his life, when his unrelenting insistence that "we *can* do it" inspired his associates to get bromine from sea water. As a very young man he had even proposed getting gold out of the ocean—which may be chemically possible but not yet, at least, commercially feasible. Professor Smith of Case used to twit him about this gold notion whenever he thought Herbert Dow's imagination was bolting away with him. Dow was a man of a million or so ideas, some of which struck his associates at first glance as superbly preposterous. These were often the very ideas he got them to make work.

they would be similar to our old chlorine cells, which are not equal to those of our competitors.

It must not be supposed that, in altering his cell system to make chlorine and caustic, Herbert Dow was trying merely to *catch up to* his competitors. His aim was to get chlorine and caustic more cheaply than they did, and this is where the second and third products of his vacuum evaporators came in. Let's see first what happened to the magnesium chloride, which came off next after the salt.

This magnesium chloride had, from the start, four important uses—which is significant in light of the fact that under the old cell system all of it had been going off down the sewer. Some of it was treated with lime to produce magnesium hydroxide, which was in turn treated with sulfuric acid to make magnesium sulfate, which is Epsom salt. Up until late in 1914, practically all the Epsom salt sold in American drugstores or used in American industry had come from Europe.

Other quantities of magnesium chloride were used to make magnesium oxychloride, which in turn soon appeared as "synthetic stone" flooring in banks, office buildings, institutions, and so on. Stucco was just then becoming popular for homes and other buildings; magnesium oxychloride was used to make the stucco set harder and faster. And in the first World War, which was just beginning, it was widely used on decks of combat and other ships; unlike many other noninflammable materials, it will not give sparks when struck by metal.

Some of the magnesium chloride went also as cell feed to Dow's new magnesium cells, which were designed to get the metallic magnesium, and of which we shall hear in Chapter 19. And some was going to other companies which made metallic magnesium from it. This metal, then rare and of few uses, was in great demand during the war. Powdered or cut into very fine chips, it was put in "star shells" which were exploded in night combat to light up the battleground.

Though Dow had been thinking of magnesium products in one way or another for years, it so happened that the plant began to produce them just as the war began. Knowing only too well the years of background behind most chemical projects, Dow was much amused at the reputation his company got for having done the whole thing in a few weeks. Years later he wrote:

Almost every year between 1894 and 1912 some new scheme or modification of a previous scheme for recovering the magnesium was evolved. Some of these

Electricity en route to the chlorine cell houses shown in the background. In the foreground is a typical brine well. This picture was made about 1902.

Wagonload of bromides headed for Japan in 1908. It was such shipments of bromides to foreign countries that precipitated Dow's "bromine war" with the Germans. In the rear is the bromine plant, with its wooden "blowing-out" tower protruding from the roof.

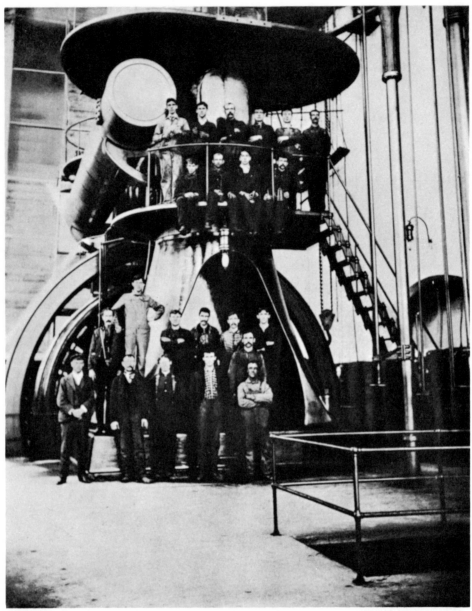

Dow powerhouse crew, 1903. However much he might economize in other matters, Herbert Dow always bought the biggest and best power equipment he could find or persuade manufacturers to build—so this generator was probably the biggest and best he could get his hands on at the time. Today, at Midland alone, the company generates and uses over a million kilowatt hours a day.

schemes never got beyond the laboratory, others were tried out in a small semi-commercial way. But in 1912 or 1913 a new process was evolved that appeared to have more commercial possibilities than any that had been evolved before, and a large plant was built for making several carloads of magnesium products a day. This plant was completed about the first of August, 1914, almost coincident with the starting of war in Europe, and within three weeks of this time we were selling magnesium chloride in New York City.[5] The reputation the Dow Company got for speedy work is as remarkable as the story of Aladdin and his lamp. In one case a young chemist approached a financial man with a proposition for making picric acid. The business man said the war would be over before he could get his plant built and asked him how long he estimated it would take him to build his picric acid plant. He replied that The Dow Chemical Company, which was located in the backwoods of Michigan, had succeeded in selling magnesium chloride in New York City within three weeks after the war had been declared in Europe, and that it certainly would be very conservative for him to accomplish the same purpose on the Hackensack meadows where he already had a building and where all necessary supplies could be brought in from stocks already in the neighborhood. However, the financial man had his doubts, and I never heard how long it took that chemist to build that picric acid plant.

Meanwhile calcium chloride, forced from the brine in the last battery of evaporators, remained to be exploited. Beginning late in 1916, this unpicturesque but useful chemical became what it has been for years—one of the company's biggest-volume wares. Whole trainloads of it leave the plant every week to do jobs all over the country. Calcium chloride has almost a genius for picking up water or moisture, and hundreds of thousands of tons are used on the nation's roads as a "stabilizer." In summer it lays dust by pulling moisture out of the air; in winter it melts ice by lowering its freezing point, and then absorbs the water. It is used as a dust-layer in operations like coal mining; sprayed on outdoor stocks of industrial coal, it minimizes troublesome "dusting" and freezing. It is used, dissolved in water, in thousands and thousands of tractor tires instead of air: the weight of the water gives the tires a firm grip on the soil, and the calcium chloride dissolved in it keeps it from freezing. It sells as a solid, a solution, or as the famous Dowflake, which is especially efficient and easy to handle. It is widely used, too, where large-scale refrigeration is called for: in meat-packing houses, storage houses for fresh fruits and vegetables, ice plants, and so on.

[5] Up to this time all the magnesium chloride ($MgCl_2$) used in this country had been coming from Germany. More than any one man, it was Herbert Dow who broke the German control of magnesium both as a chemical and as a metal.

Besides all these marketable items obtained as by-products in the new chlorine process, the company at first sold also some plain sodium chloride, or salt. But not for long: every ounce of it was soon to be needed as "feed" for the cells that broke it down into chlorine and caustic soda.

IN THE MIDST of all this, Herbert Dow made what was probably the most important business decision of his whole career. He took the company out of the bleach business.

On the surface, that seemed a startling and strange thing to do. It was to make bleach that the company had been organized in 1897. The product had for years been the company's chief source of bread and butter. The market for it was now wider and surer than ever; profits, though not large, were certain. There were sentimental considerations, too: Herbert Dow had been one of the chief founders of the American bleach industry, and one of its chief defenders when it was attacked from abroad. He had, in a word, founded the company on bleach and kept the company alive by keeping its bleach business alive. And now, of his own accord, he was giving the business up.

The last bleach was made at Midland in the summer of 1915; the last shipment, a whole trainload, was used as a disinfectant after a flood. No contracts were made with customers for 1916: all were turned over to erstwhile competitors. As if to make the decision irrevocable, the company's bleach plants were torn down.

The move had, at the time, all the earmarks of a gamble—which in many ways it was. It is necessary, however, to understand just what Herbert Dow had in mind. Back in 1895, when he was soliciting backing for his little Dow Process Company, letters *to* him mentioned *bleach*, letters *from* him mentioned *chlorine*. In short, Herbert Dow never had looked on himself as a bleach manufacturer, but as a chlorine manufacturer who sold bleach because that was at the time the way to sell chlorine. Now, after twenty years of seeking and sometimes finding, he was convinced he had better ways of using his chlorine—and would soon be finding still better ways. As Dr. E. O. Barstow explained later:

By this time Herbert Dow could see that carbon tetrachloride and chloroform and lead arsenate [6] and other things using chlorine were going to be a pretty

---

[6] Lead arsenate and lime sulfur, both insecticides, have been made at the Dow plant since 1910. They were in fact the start of the company's line of agricultural chemicals, which now also includes weed killers, soil fumigants, and plant hormones.

good gamble. Herbert Dow was a very shrewd guesser on things like that. For instance, every other large chemical company had in the old days, and also today, one or more sulfuric acid plants. The Dow Company doesn't have one, and never has made its own sulfuric acid, one reason being that we have found many ways to get around using it. In making arsenic acid, which a lot of other companies make, we used chlorine gas to chlorinate to arsenic acid. Everybody else used nitric acid. We worked out a way of making Epsom salts without sulfuric acid, and finally worked out a way to make phenol without sulfuric acid. The company also worked out a way to make aniline from ammonia and monochlorbenzene instead of benzene and nitric acid.

This was of course only a fraction of all that happened as a result of Herbert Dow's final decision to *use* his chlorine from his new cell system instead of *selling* it. Today The Dow Chemical Company is probably the world's largest producer of chlorine, but sells a bare 10 per cent of it *as chlorine*. Instead it is used, right in the plants, to make hundreds of chlorinated products—some of them by the millions of pounds. In setting up a new cell system to get cheaper and more plentiful chlorine, Herbert Dow had not been content to catch up to the procession. He had headed instead for the very front rank, where his company has remained ever since.

14

DOW SYNTHESIZES INDIGO

The outbreak of the first world war in 1914 produced a curious situation in the American chemical industry. It also produced an odd misconception that is still not quite dead.

This misconception was that the American chemical industry, including The Dow Chemical Company, owes its birth to World War I.

The fact is that by 1914 American chemical factories were, *on a tonnage basis,* outproducing the chemical factories of any country in the world, including Germany. The fact also is that this tonnage consisted largely of simple inorganic chemicals which are important but of which the public seldom hears. For some of the more complex *organic* chemicals of which the public did hear—the new coal-tar medicines and dyes, for instance—dependence was almost entirely on Germany.

It might be interesting to examine briefly the background of this dependence, which was pretty much world-wide. In 1856 the English chemist W. H. Perkin proved in his laboratory that organic dyes could be synthesized from coal tar.[1] A couple of years later, a factory to manufacture such dyes was opened in England. A few years after that, a wave of German chemical "students" descended on England, stayed a while, and returned to Germany. Soon after *that,* and exactly a dozen years after Perkin's discovery, here was the international box score on the annual production of synthetic coal-tar dyes:

Germany	$12,000,000
England	2,200,000
Switzerland	1,400,000
France	800,000
United States	0

[1] This was the birth of the aniline or coal-tar branch of the chemical industry, which today produces, or helps produce, so many synthetic dyes, medicines, perfumes, and other chemicals. And this was the Perkin for whom the coveted Perkin

By 1913, Germany was producing 80 per cent of the world's dyes, and supplying almost all of the ingredients for the remaining 20 per cent. That is not to say that American chemical manufacturers had not tried to break this German monopoly of the vast United States market for dyes. Four American dye companies had actually gone into production as early as the 1880's. But by 1913 there were only two left, and both were having a hard time surviving the price-cutting tactics of the German dye trust. Pleas for a protective tariff to enable American chemical manufacturers at least to get started were drowned out by American textile manufacturers—the chief users of dyes.

In 1906, Herbert Dow, already facing a war of survival with the German bromine cartel, proposed giving the German dye trust a tussle by synthesizing indigo, then the chief of the synthetic dyes. He had his eye especially on the beautiful brom-indigoes—for which he had quantities of the necessary bromine available. This first project never got out of the laboratory. Aside from technical difficulties, he could get no financial support to challenge the already entrenched German dye interests. Nor would the textile men even hear of a protective tariff to give him or anyone else a fighting chance to do so.

Beginning in 1914, with the German invasion of Belgium, the picture began to change. England declared war on Germany, the world's chief source of dyestuffs, and threw a maritime blockade around it. American textile men assured themselves and one another that this blockade would not apply to dyestuffs; it was assumed the English would not dare antagonize a powerful segment of United States industry by denying it something it wanted.

This quaint reasoning, after presumably giving the Germans a laugh, suggested itself to them as a bargaining point. They themselves threatened to embargo the export of their own dyes, promising to reconsider if American textile men would bring pressure on the American State Department to bring pressure on the British Admiralty to lift its blockade.[2] Meanwhile Count von Bernstorff, German Ambassador to Washington, was sending this cable to the Wilhelmstrasse:

Medal for chemical achievement is named. The medal was awarded in 1930 to Herbert Dow for his accomplishments in industrial chemistry, including many in the organic field we here see unfolding.

[2] It would be interesting to know how this proposal would have struck First Sea Lord Winston Churchill, whose navy was doing the blockading.

Serial No. 432 of March 13, 1915. It is reported to me by Hossenfelder, telegram No. 4, that the stock of dyes in this country is so small that by a German embargo about 4,000,000 American workmen might be thrown out of employment. (Signed) BERNSTORFF.

In the meantime, in its issue of December 28, 1914, one of the country's leading financial newspapers had firmly placed the blame for the dye shortage where it felt it belonged:

Users of dyestuffs in quantity are more or less indignant over the fact that the manufacturers of this country are dependent upon other countries, and Germany particularly, for the dye supply. They ask, "Why haven't our chemical companies experimented sufficiently to produce synthetic dyes, pharmaceutical products, essential oils, and synthetic perfumes, in the production of which Germany seems to have almost a monopoly?" They state that the interests of the manufacturers of the country should be placed ahead of large immediate profits and unusual dividend returns to the stockholders.

Just what "large immediate profits and unusual dividend returns to stockholders" the chemical industry had been making is not very clear. Herbert Dow, for instance, had barely managed to bring his company through the bleach and bromine wars and the financial panic of 1907, the effects of which were still being felt. Nor had those same years been too happy financially for his competitors.

So much for the blame-fixing and other emotional aspects of the dye famine. Meanwhile, something needed to be done about the shortage, which had caused great public excitement about chemicals. Promoters took in thousands upon thousands of dollars for stock in companies that were going to make green dye from grass, yellow dye from banana skins, and an attractive line of reds, golds, and browns from autumn leaves. While this pseudo chemistry—in which presumably no actual chemists took part— was getting nowhere, purchasing agents were scouring the country and the world for any dyes already in existence. Unused stocks of German indigo, for instance, were located in China, Japan, Hong Kong, and British India, purchased at four times the normal price, and resold for whatever the traffic would stand. Salesmen's samples, ordinarily given away, were sold at incredible prices; odds and ends found here and there sold at a hundred or more times their original value. Partly as a "needle," the German submarine *Deutschland* landed a couple of cargoes of dyes in this country, doling them out bit by bit at fantastic prices.

While all this was going on, serious chemists like Herbert Dow were approaching the problem as chemists. The Dow Chemical Company elected to work on the synthesis of indigo and was the first American company to succeed in this difficult problem. As a result of this and similar success in other companies, the United States emerged from the war with an organic chemical industry of its own. This eventually and for all time put an end to the American inferiority complex, long so carefully cultivated by the Germans, in regard to organic chemistry. It also gave us, eventually, hundreds of synthetic dyes, fabrics, foodstuffs, medicines and plastics—some of which are not found at all in nature, and some of which are vast improvements on what is found in nature.

Herbert Dow and his company did not come to the synthesis of indigo as tyros in organic chemistry. Especially during the prewar period covered in Chapter 12, they had succeeded in synthesizing a couple of dozen organic chemicals that were then difficult to make. And in manufacturing carbon tetrachloride and making chloroform from it, they had devised one of the first large-scale organic syntheses operated in this country.

Of all the dyes which the company could have selected to synthesize, indigo was probably the most difficult. The German dye industry, with all its experience at organic chemistry and free interchange of patents and information, had been years in learning to make synthetic indigo. Why then did Herbert Dow choose this particular problem to work on? The main reason probably was that indigo was one of the most-used of dyes, and therefore provided a tempting market. Furthermore, indigo can be treated with bromine to make a whole series of beautiful brom-indigo dyes—for which there was also a big market and for which he had the bromine ready to hand. Considerations like these made difficulties just something to be pushed aside.

A team of Dow chemists began laboratory work on the synthesis of indigo in the summer of 1915. The group was headed by Professor Lee H. Cone, who had come from the University of Michigan for the purpose. By October, Herbert Dow was writing to Dr. A. W. Smith:

The best new thing in sight is indigo. Every step has been worked out and they are turning out a few ounces regularly every day, and there is nothing in the whole proposition from beginning to end that is going to call for any great amount of money or that appears to be problematical.

Herbert Dow's letters were ordinarily masterpieces of hardheaded exactitude. The above paragraph was, however, practically a distillate of wistful thinking. Dow was so eager to be making indigo that he merely assumed that "every step has been worked out"; and there was something very optimistic indeed in his overlooking the fact that making a few ounces a day of a difficult product in the laboratory is not the same as making hundreds of pounds of it in the factory. And as to its not calling for "any great amount of money," this protest arrived from Dr. Smith, who was, of course, one of the directors, by return mail:

I was sorry not to have had an opportunity to talk with you relative to . . . the large expenditure planned for the indigo plant. It seems to me that . . . so large an investment in the indigo plant is not warranted by the present experimental development. However, as I had not had an opportunity to go over this with you previous to the meeting, I did not oppose the authorization. . . . I think a mistake was made in going so fast.

It might almost be that Dr. Smith, who was an expert and doggedly realistic chemist, had not had "an opportunity to go over this with you previous to the meeting" because Herbert Dow had avoided giving him such an opportunity. Dow was so sure he had the indigo problem licked, and so eager to get into the hungry indigo market, that he did not want any conservative-minded considerations slowing him up. In any case, he wrote back, again by return post:

You speak of so large an investment in the indigo plant not being warranted by the present experimental development. I think you are not aware of the extent of the experimental development. The yields of every step in the process have been determined under many variations of conditions and a good many pounds of indigo have been made, and if on a large scale we obtain an average yield of the good and the poor, it will be an extremely profitable investment, and there is no reason why we should not obtain the good yields, as results are consistent and the factors that cause poor yields are, in the main, understood.

Dr. Smith wrote back unhappily that he had just run into Dr. Cone on a streetcar, and was only too aware of the extent of the experimental development. And Dr. Cone strongly agreed, Dr. Smith told Dow, that

. . . it is very decidedly desirable to build first a small plant, say about one hundred pounds per day, previous to building a larger plant. This need not deter you from ordering the materials for the larger plant, as most of them could be used for other purposes if not needed for indigo. The indigo proposition really seems the most difficult of many that might be tried. For that reason possibly the time and energy spent on that could be more profitably spent in making some of the other numerous organic chemicals that are very high-priced and whose manufacture would be decidedly simpler.

It seems pretty clear that Dr. Smith was hoping that Herbert Dow would give up his indigo project altogether. Or, if he did insist on pursuing it, Dr. Smith hoped to persuade him to follow the routine and orderly steps followed in going into any new process. This meant getting the process first *really* worked out in the laboratory, then trying it on a modest commercial scale in a small "pilot" plant, and then attempting full-scale production. The reasons behind this traditional procedure are not hard to perceive. Chemicals are like people: they don't always behave as they theoretically should. A process that runs smooth as a daydream in a laboratory may become, in the factory, a nightmare of hitches, balks, and frustrations. And a process that works on a small scale in the factory may choose to buck and rear in unpredictable manner when tried on a large scale. None of this was of course any news to Herbert Dow. But he wanted to get indigo on the market fast and so he simply decided to lay the usual procedure aside—and did lay it aside.[3]

The process which he counted on to work—and which finally did work—involved a series of steps. Some of these were, considering the day and the equipment available, pretty hard at first to handle on an efficient mass-production basis. But in December of 1916, eighteen months after work had begun on this problem which had taken the Germans long years to solve, the first shipment of American-made synthetic indigo left the Dow plant. Two other American companies, Du Pont and National Aniline, were also soon in production. As Dr. Mark Putnam wrote later:

This accomplishment, while important from an economic standpoint, was even more important from a moral standpoint because it tended to remove the heretofore strong doubts as to whether America could produce a self-contained and

[3] As the reader must have begun to suspect, it was part of Herbert Dow's character to insist more often than not on doing things his own way. It is evident in this case that he had given himself the additional luxury of confronting his directors with a *fait accompli*. Instead of arguing in advance that they should set up a big indigo plant, he had gone on and spent the money to set it up. This made any dispute about whether he had done right a somewhat academic discussion. Both he and Dr. Smith of course realized this, but went on and had the discussion anyway. It did no harm, and it had no perceptible effect on Herbert Dow's custom of doing things his own way. He was a pioneer in a pretty much uncharted industry, and pioneers don't get very far by letting too many people tell them too often which way to turn. "He made us rich in spite of ourselves," one of his early stockholders once remarked of him.

vigorous dye and organic chemical industry. . . . The American dye industry is now one of the most complete and important in the world.[4]

This first Dow indigo was sold in the traditional form of a 20 per cent paste, and at $1.50 a pound. This was, at the start, less than it cost to make. By the end of the war, barely two years later, improvements in the process had brought the price down to 75 cents, including a profit. Within five years Dow and his competitors were producing a total of twenty-eight million pounds a year and selling it at 26 cents a pound; within a couple of years more the price had been lowered to 14 cents a pound. This was less than the Germans, with all their dye-making experience, had ever been able to charge. Dow indigo went, as it still does, all over this country and into many markets abroad that had also been monopolized by the Germans.

Thus Herbert Dow had borne a firm hand in upsetting another foreign chemical monopoly in American and world markets. But meanwhile he and other American chemical manufacturers had a more significant job to do. The world was in flames from German military aggression, and the young American chemical industry was being called on to perform what were for the day some miraculous feats.

[4] *Twenty-Five Years of Chemical Engineering Progress* (American Institute of Chemical Engineers, 1933).

DOW SERVES IN
WORLD WAR I

The first world war began in August of 1914; the United States entered it in April of 1917. In the two and a half years between those dates, a great many people became only too glad to revise some of their negative fixed ideas about the country's chemical industry.

One of these ideas, as we have seen, was that the German chemical industry was so far ahead of ours that it was hopeless for ours to catch up. This notion had two important corollaries:

1. American plants could not hope to produce, in the *vast quantities* which modern warfare requires, such staple raw materials as chlorine, bromine, caustic soda, phenol, and so on.
2. American plants could not hope to produce, in quantity or at all, certain organic or otherwise complicated chemicals that had always come from Europe.

The source of such negative notions was not far to seek. Up until the dye panic of 1914, the general public was hardly aware that an American chemical industry existed. Chemical companies were few, small, and for the most part owned by families rather than armies of stockholders, as now.[1] Few products these companies made reached the public directly; hardly any of their scientific advances came to public notice at all. In Germany, where chemistry was a sort of proud national project, important discoveries were announced on the front pages of newspapers. In America, news of such discoveries seldom got out of the plant.[2] Naturally, people were not going to expect miracles from an industry they hardly knew was in existence.

[1] The U. S. Census of 1910 listed the chemical industry as having 27,600 employees, capitalization of $155,100,000, annual sales of $117,700,000.

[2] Because they were business secrets. American chemical manufacturers were and still are ardent competitors. The German industry had already been cartelized into one big monopolistic family. No competition was permitted among members in matters of patents, products, markets, or prices. The chemical pie was cut up behind closed doors, and customers paid what they were told for the pieces.

Another source of doubt about the industry's ability to meet the challenge of war was hardly so innocent. This source consisted of certain members of the small army of sales representatives kept in this country by the Ger-

---

THE STAG HOTEL
(The Company Boarding House)

——

Advantages:

Best board in the city.

120 clean and comfortable beds.

Large room for reading, table games, letter writing, etc.

Electric fan cooling system in operation during hot weather.

Convenient Meal Hours.

5:40 a. m., 7:30 a m., 11.40 a. m.; 4:40 p. m., 5:40 p. m.

Shower baths, with soap and towel free to patrons of the hotel; 10c to all others.

Rates:

$6.50 per week to Company employees; $7.50 per week for all others.   Credit until pay day.

Single meals 35c; single lodging 25c.

Meal ticket good thirty days; 21 meals $6 00

===

If you wish to board at the Hotel, get a slip signed by your foreman.

Wartime accommodations. Production demands on the plant in World War I made Midland a pretty crowded place, and the company helped maintain the Stag Hotel. The company also financed the building of homes for sale or rent to employees.

man chemical houses. Incredible as it may seem, the whispered and even bellowed "doubts" of these men were accepted at face value in some very high places, including, for a while, Congress. These men were able, for instance, to make Congress hesitate to put suitable protective duties on American-produced coal-tar dyes and medicinals. Their argument was that Americans could never learn to make the things right anyhow, and so the end result of the tariff would be to make the German products cost more in this country when the war was over. These people also managed to blackmail some American distributors and users of dyestuffs and medicinals into not encouraging native producers. The threat was that anyone doing so would be barred from ever receiving German chemicals again. This threat had been standard practice for years; it was apt to be trotted out whenever an American proposed making a difficult organic chemical monopolized by the Germans. Since it was not possible for the young organic branch of the industry here to make *all* these products right away, the threat had more to it than meets the eye.[3]

Fortunately, Herbert Dow and a great many men like him had been standing up to that sort of thing for years. There had been much exploration of complicated organic chemicals with which it was generally thought only the Germans could possibly have the "right touch." Dow had in fact already decided to "bet" much of his company's future on such products, as against bleach and routine bromides. He had, at the same time, worked out ways of producing what were for that day prodigious supplies of such staples as chlorine, caustic soda, and bromine. The consequence was that he and the company were able to pitch into their war assignments without being awed by them or indulging in false starts and fiascoes.

Measured by volume, Dow's two largest contributions were chlorine and caustic soda. Neither of these is a complicated or picturesque item, any more than wood and iron are, but like wood and iron they were critically needed as basic "building blocks" for war materials. The Dow plant, which up to a few years before had not produced a pound of caustic soda, turned out something like thirty million pounds of it for the war effort. What was not absolutely required for use within the plant was sold to the Government at three and one half cents a pound, as against open market prices up to ten cents a pound.

Matching this thirty million pounds of caustic soda, the Dow plant pro-

[3] It is not hard to see why. Suppose an American textile manufacturer, for instance, customarily used ten dyes, all of which he obtained from Germany. Then an American chemical manufacturer proposed making one of these dyes. If the textile man bought the native product, he might find himself deprived of access to the nine which were not yet native, and might not be for years. This threat was still very important when the war first began in 1914: it was widely assumed the German armies would soon have the thing over with, after which Americans who had "bought American" would be punished as above. Sometimes, for temporary political advantage, United States businessmen and industrialists are represented as ruthlessly eager to crush each other and exploit the public. Nervous or gullible citizens should examine some of the foreign attempts to keep this country from acquiring a real chemical industry, and get some idea of what ruthlessness really is.

duced some thirty million pounds of chlorine; most of which was used in the plant's production of vast quantities of phenol, chloroform, carbon tetrachloride, monochlorbenzene and acetic anhydride. All this caustic and chlorine of course came from the new cell system which had been put in just before the war.

By volume, Dow's next most important war product was phenol, of which carbolic acid is the liquid form. Up to this time, little phenol had been made in this country, and most of that little had been recovered from by-product coal tar at coke works. The Germans already had, after long effort, discovered a way to produce phenol synthetically. Dow was asked to produce synthetic phenol, and did. Within a short time the plant was turning out one ton a day, then three, then five, then fifteen, then thirty. In all, the plant produced some 23,500,000 pounds; a 3,000,000-pound-a-month plant, largest in the United States, was just getting into operation when the war ended.

Much of this phenol was sent to explosives plants for conversion to trinitro phenol, otherwise known as picric acid. Picric acid and TNT (trinitro toluene) were the famous "disruptive explosives" that made their big debut in this first World War. A "disruptive" is, in munitions parlance, an explosive for artillery shells that isn't set off when the shell is shot from the gun, but does go off when the shell lands. To the extent that more efficient ways of killing more people can be called an advance, the introduction and wide use of picric acid and TNT was one of its major advances.

Another of Dow's large-volume war products was of course bromine, of which he had long since become one of the country's chief producers. Some of this went into photographic film, of which great quantities were used by the armed forces for reconnaissance and other purposes. A great deal went into increased production of medicinal bromides for civilian and military use. An interesting medical use developed during the war was in the treatment of shell shock, as the emotional upsets precipitated by war strains were then generally called. The bromides were used as a calming agent.

Incidentally, the general demand for medicinal bromides greatly increased during the war. This was due in part to the nerve-strain of war, and in part to the fact that the war itself had cut off the supply of the newer sedatives, the barbitals. Most of these had been coming from Germany.

Besides meeting the increased demand for routine bromides, the company supplied the Government with one million pounds of bromine for use in gases called "lachrymators," otherwise known as tear gas. Military demand for this use was so great that seventeen additional brine wells had to be drilled and an extra power plant built to handle their flow of bromine-bearing brine. The wells and power plant were an official branch of the Army's Edgewood Arsenal, built and operated by the Dow Company for the Chemical Warfare Service, and bought by the company after the war.

The company also made vast quantities of the deadly and cruel mustard gas. This was an assignment which no one on the Dow team relished; but someone had to do it. They were selected for the job because of their known skill at working with ethylene, sulfur, and chlorine, which are combined in mustard gas as dichlorethyl sulfide. The gas was made by a process worked out by Professor A. W. Smith. At the height of production, as many as ten thousand pounds a day were made. At the war's end what remained was buried at sea.

Carbon tetrachloride was another of Dow's large-volume war products. Something like ten million pounds of it were produced, using the synthesis worked out at the Dow plant in 1902. Dow had been the first in this country to synthesize the chemical on a commercial basis; at the time this had been the largest-scale organic synthesis achieved in an American factory. Much of this ten million pounds of Dow "carbon tet" was sold as a solvent, as a fire extinguisher, and as an intermediate for various war materials. A great deal was used at the plant in the synthesis of chloroform—another major achievement from some years before. About one million pounds of chloroform were produced for military and civilian medical use, and as an organic solvent for industry.

From the modern organic chemist's viewpoint, one of the company's most picturesque and important wartime achievements was the mass production of acetic anhydride. Up to 1914, the million or so pounds of this valuable organic solvent used in this country each year had come from Germany. It became critically needed during the war for the waterproofing and strengthening of the fabric airplane wings of the day. The company was able to make what was then the colossal total of one million pounds of it, and thus was the country's largest wartime producer of this much-needed chemical.

Some of Dow's acetic anhydride went to producing acetyl salicylic acid, which is of course aspirin. Up to that time all aspirin was of German origin, but Dow made as much as 125,000 pounds of it a month, becoming and remaining ever since one of the country's chief producers of that familiar chemical. Hand in hand with this development went the manufacture of salicylic acid, achieved by Dr. Mark E. Putnam in 1915 and 1916, using phenol and carbon dioxide.

Another important Dow wartime contribution was two million pounds of monochlorbenzene, also called chlorbenzol. This went to explosives factories, where there was a crying demand for it. Chlorbenzol was one of the chlorine products Dow had "bet" on when he abandoned bleach-making, though there had been at the time little demand for it. It soon became and has been ever since a major Dow product. Some goes into the making of phenol, of which Dow makes and uses very great quantities. Some is used to make aniline; a great deal is sold to the rubber industry as a solvent.

Other important Dow wartime contributions were Epsom salt, in volume, other magnesium products, and insecticides to protect food crops. Some hexachlorethane was manufactured for smoke screens. Considerable secret research was done on combat gases and on means of defense against them.

The bulk of Dow's wartime products went to various branches of the U. S. Government, to the Ordnance Department, the Navy, the Aircraft Production Division, the Chemical Warfare Service, the American Experimental Station, and the Medical Supply Department. Quantities of medical supplies were also furnished to the Red Cross and to the Belgian Relief Commission. Especially before this country entered the war, a great deal of Dow output was sold to the purchasing commissions of the various Allied governments. Not a nickel's worth was sold to the Germans.

At the war's close the company received this citation from the War Department:

Through the co-operation of this company with the Chemical Warfare Service, the first large-scale equipment for the manufacture of ethylene, sulfur monochloride, and mustard gas was obtained. The company furnished detailed design of apparatus for the manufacture of certain secret products. Its staff developed much of this country's information with respect to the manufacture of mustard gas. It furnished free use of its processes and its accumulated experience in the procurement of bromine brines largely without compensation and it is believed at some financial loss. It is very gratifying to be enabled to transmit this visible recognition of patriotic war service.[4]

Such were the main contributions of the young Dow Chemical Company to the winning of the nation's first World War. Though small in comparison with what was contributed in the second World War, they were almost incredibly large for the time. And they surprised, both in volume and range,

[4] In World War II the company was to reveal to peacetime competitors and others its knowledge of the making of metallic magnesium and of styrene, basis of much of the postwar plastics industry. This knowledge had been gathered at the cost of untold money and years of research.

Corner of "Old Mill" Laboratory. So much has been said of Herbert Dow's predilection for research that the reader may suppose that research was as elaborately housed and equipped as it is now. However, some of the company's most outstanding early achievements were worked out on the kind of jury-rigged apparatus here shown. In 1910 Professor Smith wrote Dow: "My observation about the laboratory was that all the work was being done at the hood in one corner, where the chemists were in each other's way. Another hood or two would remedy this. The floor was poor and could not be kept clean, and is used as a highway. Covering with linoleum would correct this. The bleach sampler tramped in frequently with bleach on his shoes, which did not help the cleanliness of the place. This can easily be remedied by keeping him out. The table tops are so corroded as to make it impossible to keep them clean. They should be planed down, or, better, covered with glass or rubber. The latter would be comparatively inexpensive."

Vista on Dow Grounds, showing house. Much of the shrubbery in the foreground was probably planted by Dow, an ardent week-end horticulturist. The house was built in 1899; the planting went on for the next thirty years.

Dowmetal castings, as of 1927. Behind this repertory of castings were eight years of metallurgical research which Dow had to do because no one else would do it. Dow had hoped that if he manufactured and alloyed magnesium, users would come forward and develop techniques for fabricating it. They didn't—so he did.

a great many people who had thought American chemical companies were not very able.

Part of this accomplishment was of course due to Herbert Dow's foresight in building up an expert and enterprising team of research and production chemists—which was his idea of a chemical company. Part was due, too, to the earnest and patriotic spirit of the working force. About one person in five in the Midland area had been born in Germany or was of parents who had been born in Germany. Many of these people worked in the Dow plant. Nevertheless, not one act of sabotage or disloyalty is known to have occurred in or about the plant.

There was however one "incident" which looked for a while as if it were going to be serious. A few German saboteurs were known to be loose in the country, and had contrived to do some random damage. Naturally, there was a possibility that they might turn their attentions to the Dow plant. A strong fence was therefore built around the plant and kept floodlighted at night and patrolled by a force of guards hired for the purpose. For months nothing happened; and then one night two of the guards discovered, with suitable excitement, a hole big enough for a man to crawl through dug under a remote part of the fence. A day or so later it came out that the two guards had themselves dug the hole in order to discover it. They had been afraid the plant was so safe that they would lose their jobs. They did.

During the war, the working force at the plant passed the two thousand mark for the first time. Most of these people already had homes in and around Midland; but some were from other localities. Herbert Dow was always greatly concerned for the comfort of those who worked with him, whether they were famous chemists or just swept up the floors. He therefore caused to be put up, at considerable expense to the company, several hundred houses for rent or sale to employees. He also largely financed a low-priced hotel for employees. This was called the Stag Hotel and was certainly no Waldorf-Astoria, but a great many people lived there in comfort. And it was one of the few "concentrations" of people that during the deadly influenza epidemic of the winter of 1918–1919 did not produce a single case of the disease.

It was during the war, too, that Herbert Dow and Dr. Barstow took the initiative in setting up a community recreation center in Midland. In addition to the good which this did in Dow's lifetime, it served as a groundwork for the considerably expanded community recreation program carried forward by his son, the late Willard Dow, and very much in operation today. Part of this is an elaborate community music program, which has been widely used as a model all over the country. Undertakings of this sort were part of these men's character, and they were doing this kind of thing long before it became a common practice in industry.

As in every war, there were in this one companies which made a very great deal of money by selfishly exploiting the critical needs of the armed forces and of civilians. As was inevitable, The Dow Chemical Company was accused by a few individuals of having done just that. Whenever Herbert Dow heard of such accusations, and suspected that the accuser really believed them, he took pains to set before the accuser a number of facts that were not publicly known.

Typical of this was his reply to the physician who had complained of the rise in price of Dow potassium bromide during the war. Dow explained in careful detail how the price he had to pay for the potash rose almost over-night from 4 cents to $2.05 a pound—and how his efforts to produce potash himself had been selfishly blocked. In this same letter he mentioned that some of his potassium bromide had fallen among speculators, who charged up to 300 per cent profit for themselves. The letter went on to say:

It will probably be of interest to you to know that when our country became involved in the war we placed at its disposal our entire plant, and at its request many chemical products were manufactured upon which no profit was taken. The market price of our stock declined over 50 per cent from the time the United States entered the war until the armistice.

This Company was one of the first in the country to be awarded the Certificate of Merit by the Government as a testimonial for its services. Our entire transactions with the Government were audited by The Cleveland Trust Company and disclosed that the net profit of our Company upon the U. S. Government contracts was less than 1¾ per cent, which amounted to less than 1 per cent a year. Our course of conduct in dealings with the Government is probably not excelled by any other company in the country.

We feel certain that your criticism was innocently made through misapprehension of the true facts; and we trust you will accept this letter in the spirit in which it is written.

HERBERT H. DOW

So much for the facts of the war and its repercussions in Midland. Meanwhile, with the war's sudden and unexpected end in November of 1918, Herbert Dow and his company were confronted with a set of economic facts they had better not misapprehend if they wanted to stay in the chemical business.

16

SURVIVING THE
WAR ACHIEVEMENT

AMERICAN INDUSTRIAL CHEMISTS ARE APT TO GET A BIT GLASSY OF EYE WHEN assured, as they so often are, that the first World War created this country's chemical industry. The fact is that the war came, in a way, very near wrecking the industry. And few major companies had to fight harder to survive their wartime achievements than did The Dow Chemical Company. Here was an instance, if ever there was one, where the only thing as costly as losing a war is helping to win it.

On paper, the company came out of the war rich. Assets totaled almost six million dollars. But that was on paper. Actually, a great many of these dollars were tied up in war-expanded plant equipment, for which there was now little or no immediate work to do. A great many dollars were tied up in vast stockpiles of such war-needed materials as phenol and caustic soda, for which there was now little sale. And a great many were tied up in "accounts receivable"—sums due from the Government or from other companies which were in turn creditors of the Government. All of these accounts were "good"—it was just a question of collecting them. The war had ended almost as unexpectedly as it had begun. Production had gone on right up to the brink of the Armistice, and then been shut down almost overnight. This was both Government's and Industry's first experience of demobilizing from a total war, and the confusion and pressure in the financial departments of both were terrific. The art of getting up maddeningly complicated forms for businessmen to fill out was then in its infancy. But it was a lusty infancy; and when no more complicated form could be thought up to confront the businessman with, he could always be required to fill out the same one over and over, a little differently each time.

But the big problem at Dow—as in most of the chemical plants in the country—was the abrupt cancellation of market for the very products the plant had been geared up to make in vast quantity during the war. Typical was what happened with phenol. Up to 1914, the country used maybe one million pounds of phenol a year, practically all of it from abroad. By 1918, the country's plants were able to produce one hundred million pounds a year, and there were 27,000,000 pounds already on hand. This looked like enough phenol to last for a good many years. The economic outlook for the chemical was particularly glum at Dow, which had been producing much of it. There were 4,000,000 pounds stored at Midland; the new 3,000,000-pound-a-month plant there, just going into operation as the war ended, had to be dismantled.

Caustic soda was another big economic problem at Midland. During the war it had been a vitally important product; now there was more of it around than anyone knew what to do with. This was especially unfortunate at Dow, for the cells which had been put in a few years ago could not produce chlorine without producing a proportionate amount of caustic soda. What could not be used in the plant or sold on the flooded market outside became a storage or even a disposal problem. And as for metallic magnesium, for which Herbert Dow had cherished such high peacetime hopes, there was no market at all. Even mustard gas, though no one was sorry to see it go, represented a vast hole in plant investment. Nor could the skill and valuable organic chemicals invested in the gas be in any way recovered: no means could be found to get the chemicals back out of the gas, and it all had to be shipped out to sea and buried.

Meanwhile, some wartime products did hold up well enough to keep the company going, though with only a fraction of its wartime personnel.[1] Bromides, for instance, continued to do well; and so did indigo, aspirin, salicylic acid, lime sulfur, lead arsenate, and carbon tetrachloride. Profits from these were not large and a serious industrial slump was shaping up. But at least the company was managing to stay in business, which was more than a great many chemical companies which had served well in the war were contriving to do. Some simply folded; some voluntarily formed mergers with kindred companies; some were bought up by companies which were surviving the postwar slump better. This period has in fact been called "The Merger Era" of American industrial chemistry. It was during

[1] To minimize unemployment, a great many employees went on a four-day work week. The company fared much better during the long depression of the nineteen-thirties, when Midland became famous as "the town that doesn't know there's a depression going on." Thanks to the exploratory research Herbert Dow had always insisted on, products and employment steadily increased in this period.

this period that chemical companies in general changed from closely held family enterprises to larger, publicly held corporations. The very few chemical companies which today outrank The Dow Chemical Company in size acquired at this time a great deal of size by merger or buying up smaller companies.[2]

Herbert Dow attacked his share of the problem with characteristic directness. As he saw it, the most promising answer lay in *research*, especially research along organic lines. He had, as we remember, already done a great deal of exploring along these lines, particularly in the period beginning around 1909. Most of the products then evolved found at the time little or no market. Then the war had come, affecting this research program in several ways at once. On the one hand, it had cut short the search for new organic products that might or might not prove of commercial use. On the other, it called for what were then great quantities of organic products that had hitherto come largely from Germany: phenol, indigo, acetic anhydride, the salicylates, and so on. The war not only *demanded* that Americans like Dow produce these chemicals: it for several years prevented the German cartels, with their vicious price-cutting and other punitive techniques, *from keeping Americans like Dow from producing them.*

Thus the end of actual hostilities with Germany left organic research at Midland in a curious predicament. The wartime achievement in indigo and the salicylates and so on had shown that such research *would* pay off if given a chance. But the shooting was now over, though the actual peace treaty with Germany was not to come till several years later. This meant that Germany was still technically an enemy, and only the traditional "trading with the enemy" embargo was keeping the German chemical cartels from flooding this country with cut-priced chemicals that might well wipe out most of the organic business that manufacturers like Dow had built up or were contemplating building up. This danger of cut-priced "dumping" was all the greater because the Germans were artfully proposing to pay part of their reparations in chemicals—a proposition that was very seductive to a great many industrial consumers of these chemicals, who saw a chance to stock up very cheaply. The real bill would of course come in

[2] An excellent discussion of this phase of the industry can be found in William Haynes' *American Chemical Industry: A History*, Vol. IV (D. Van Nostrand Company, Inc., New York). Most industries had already gone through this phase; it was not till its war performance that the public in general became aware of the chemical industry's promise as a widely useful and profitable activity.

later, when the Germans had re-established their monopoly here and could charge monopoly prices again.

All this is mentioned to indicate that Herbert Dow's postwar decision to go on "betting" on all-out research was more of a gamble than would appear on the surface. The German organic chemical industry had been neither damaged nor strained during the war. Vast stockpiles of some synthetic dyes, medicinals, and other organic products had been built up. With the German mark approaching worthlessness, wages and salaries almost nothing in real money, and the demand for dollars great, stockpiles and current product could be dumped abroad at murderously low prices. It is not hard to see how this could negate whatever success Dow's postwar research program might have. But he had fought all his life, and he was ready to climb in the ring again. His plan of campaign followed three specific lines at once:

1. Research to improve and increase production of chemicals already being made.
2. Research aimed at creating new products, or finding new uses for old ones.
3. Crusading, along with other leaders of the industry, for a protective tariff to forestall German dumping and price-cutting until the industry could handle the problem in stride by itself.

This time the directorate of the company "went along" with him in a body. Since 1897, the year of the company's founding, he had been general manager, and as such had actively run the organization. Now, in 1918, he became president also; he served in both capacities till his death in 1930. Albert E. Convers, president from 1897 till 1918, became chairman of the board of directors, and served in that office till his death in 1935.

Hitherto the bulk of the research effort had fallen on men like Dr. Strosacker and Dr. Barstow, who also had plants to run. One of the first acts of the new president was to take some of the load off these men by setting up a formal Organic Research Laboratory, headed by Dr. William J. Hale. Dr. Hale brought to Midland such men as Dr. E. C. Britton and William H. Williams. These men, and their associates, played leading roles in Dow's new research program. It was at this time, too, that the company's library was begun: today it has on hand some thirty thousand technical volumes, some five hundred periodicals, and is said to be one of the largest of its kind in the United States.[3]

[3] Several of the volumes are, appropriately enough, by Dr. Hale, who in 1934 became Research Consultant and began writing a series of perceptive books about chemistry's part in human life. Dr. E. C. Britton succeeded him as Director of Or-

Within a few years, the stepped-up interest in product and method research had the plant working at capacity again, and then expanding. The wartime manufacture of mustard gas, for example, had involved the production of ethylene. Ethylene is today one of the most-used of chemicals: it goes by the hundreds of millions of pounds each year into one compound or another. But back in 1920, there was little or no demand for these compounds. Dow tried in that year to market ethylene through such products as ethylene chlorohydrin, ethylene oxide, and ethylene glycol. These products were eventually to be used by the trainload. Ethylene became the starting point for a whole series of solvents and for a number of organic syntheses; glycol also has numerous volume uses. But at the time, no use for them could be found; and, as before the war, work on them was temporarily laid aside.

Here, of course, Dow was up against the problem which generally confronts the chemical manufacturer when he undertakes to make and market new chemicals. Aside from devising an economical and efficient way of making them, he must very often discover and promote definite uses for them. When the new product is in itself a finished "consumer product"—a fabric, for instance, that he can advertise directly to the public—the promotional task is often difficult (and expensive) enough. The difficulty is usually many times greater when the product cannot be sold as it stands, but must be used by another manufacturer as an ingredient of a finished product that *he* is going to undertake to make and sell. Such a man is not subject to the charms of expensive four-color advertisements or the suave exhortations of radio commercials. He thinks sternly in terms of dollars, cents, and fractions of cents; he does a great deal of hardheaded figuring before he spends money on somebody's new chemical.

A dismal experience of Herbert Dow's with ethylene glycol illustrates the sort of unhappy thing that can happen during these hunts for uses for new chemicals. Dynamite is made from nitroglycerin; the dynamite of that day had a dangerous way of freezing in winter, and exploding without

ganic Research. Today the company's multifarious research activities are coordinated by an Executive Research Committee of which Dr. W. R. Veazey is chairman. Incidentally, these moves toward the formalizing of Dow research do not mean that men like Dr. Barstow, Dr. Strosacker, and Dr. Putnam stopped looking for and finding very important new products and production methods. In fact, a good way to get in hot water around Midland is to make some statement to the contrary. These men won't say anything but each has a vehemently loyal team of associates who will say plenty.

notice as it thawed out. Dow research demonstrated that when the nitro-glycerin is made with glycol, the dynamite will not freeze. Herbert Dow spent months trying to convince a big explosives company that it should therefore use glycol (which he would supply) to make its nitroglycerin. The explosives people kept insisting that they knew about glycol already, and considered that using it here would cause more difficulties than it would solve. Presently the explosives company changed its mind, but bought its glycol elsewhere. On top of this, another company discovered and patented a completely obvious use for glycol that no one at Dow had thought of. This was as a principal ingredient in antifreeze for automobile radiators—a use in which it sold by the millions of pounds. Herbert Dow characteris-tically took all the blame for this double fiasco, and it was years before he stopped kicking himself for it.

Meanwhile, other postwar research projects were proving more fruitful. Production of indigo and the salicylates was improved and expanded; the company remained what it had become during the war and is to this day—one of the world's chief producers of these two important products, which had so long been German monopolies. Great progress was made on such "aromatic" chemicals as synthetic oil of wintergreen, coumarin, and para-dichlorbenzene; products which a few years before no one would have expected to see coming from an American factory. These and many other new Dow products involved ethylene and chlorobenzene; the new products developed so many cousins and descendants that ethylene and chloroben-zene presently became as important in the Dow operation as chlorine and caustic soda.

Nor was all the success along organic lines. Automobiles were becoming numerous but paved roads were rare. Dusty roads became a nation-wide nuisance, but Dow's calcium chloride supplied the answer. The chemical was already in fairly wide use in refrigeration brines; now, as easily handled Dowflake, it was strewn on the nation's roads to hold down the dust. This it did by pulling moisture out of the air and holding it on the road. The flake product, first of its kind, was introduced in 1919 and began almost at once selling in quantity. It is still one of the company's most important bulk products, and goes from the plant by the trainload.

All these were only some of the product developments of the postwar era at Midland. Nor is their importance to be measured merely in terms of immediate or eventual dollars and cents. Perhaps still more important was the enterprising spirit behind them. Confronted by the postwar oversupply of his standard products, Herbert Dow could have chosen to sit tight till the market for them came back. Instead, he chose boldly to strike out into additional fields, creating new products, new markets, new areas of development. Not all industrialists, confronted with temporary or even permanent public apathy to the things they know how to or like to make, have the courage and vision to do this. Like some types of duck when wounded, they dive for the bottom, cling to a sunken root, and hang on till they drown. Herbert Dow would not have known how to do this. If he'd been a duck and somebody had winged him, he'd have figured out a marketable use for the lead.

Nor was all his counterattack on his postwar plight confined to the laboratory and to the factory. As early as 1918 he set up a New York sales office—first of a network that now covers the country. He began, too, going to the general public for money with which to carry out his ideas. Up to now, practically all of the company's unearned capital had come from people he knew in and around Cleveland and Midland. In January of 1923, fifteen thousand shares of nonpar stock were sold at $40 a share. This offering was the first public financing of equity money attempted by the company. This first issue was followed by others at fairly regular intervals; between 1923 and 1930, common stock was sold for a total of $3,975,000 and preferred for $1,500,000—making a grand total of $5,475,000 in new money.

A great deal of plant expansion was financed, too, by short-term bank loans. Often these loans were obtained to set up a particular process; profits from the process were used to repay the loan, generally in five years or less.[4]

Meanwhile, Herbert Dow had been fighting a battle which concerned not only his own company, but the chemical industry as a whole. Indeed, with the growing importance of chemicals in everyday life, it concerned the entire country. As we saw earlier in this chapter, there was very real danger that the Germans would take advantage of the postwar predicament of the American chemical industry to wipe out the progress its young

---

[4] The financial community has sometimes been astonished at the low rates of interest the company has usually paid for these loans: they do indeed compare rather favorably with the 8 and even 10 per cent Herbert Dow was made to pay when he first started out. For decades the guiding spirit in the company's financial affairs has been Earl W. Bennett, who began as a bookkeeper and is now chairman of the board of directors. Though he never put a chemical together in his whole life, Mr. Bennett has had much to do with The Dow Chemical Company's growth from a small bleach plant to a chemical empire worth over a quarter billion dollars.

organic branch had made. Only the embargo act left over from actual hostilities was preventing the Germans from doing this. Obviously, this embargo would presently be taken off. Along with other farsighted American chemical manufacturers, Herbert Dow joined the fight for a tariff which would protect American production till it could itself handle any attempt at German dumping or cartel-backed price cutting. This was no new fight with him; years before the war he had tried to get a suitable import duty placed on German indigo, and failed. In 1916, while setting up the first plant to achieve the synthesis of indigo in this country, he wrote:

There is no doubt but what the United States can establish a permanent dye industry if the laws will protect the American dye maker from the freezing-out tactics of foreign competitors, in the same way it would protect them against the freezing-out tactics of an American competitor. In other words, the Sherman Law makes it impossible for one company to freeze out another in ways that were attributed to Standard Oil in years gone by. But it does not protect the American manufacturer from combinations of foreign competitors who will make any price necessary in order to destroy a new dye industry in this country.

Around the same time he was testifying before the Federal Trade Commission:

Possibly the most highly organized chemical in existence is indigo. It is the most important of all the dyes. Possibly eight or nine years ago we made a little indigo in the laboratory, to see if we could make it. From time to time we have worked on the matter of intermediate products, and are today turning out one intermediate product that we did not turn out a few months ago. We have an organization now, working on indigo. It will require, however, a very large investment to complete an indigo plant, if they decide that they now know how to make it well enough so that they think they can compete; the question will then arise as to whether the price will immediately be reduced, the minute we start to manufacture.[5]

THE CHAIRMAN: By the German chemical companies?

MR. DOW: By the German organizations. All indigo is sold through a German organization. Not one pound is sold otherwise. And this applies, so far as I know, to all German chemicals.

THE CHAIRMAN: Do you know the capitalization and assets of that German cartel?

[5] The United States was not yet in the war. The Allies were not doing well, and it was generally thought the war might end any week. Hence the immediacy with which Dow speaks. Also, as he points out, the danger applies not merely to indigo, but to a great many other chemicals of which the Germans preferred to remain the world's sole source.

Mr. Dow: It is very, very great. I do not know just exactly what it is, Mr. Chairman.

The Chairman: Some four hundred and forty odd million dollars.

Herbert Dow continued to argue for protective tariff throughout the war and on into the postwar period, when it became of very immediate importance. Opponents of protection of course represented that men like Dow wanted protection in order to be able to charge higher prices. He answered this by pointing out:

The late war was the equivalent of infinite protective tariff and the chemical industries developed very rapidly, with the result that aspirin, on which the lowest wholesale price before the war was $8.00 a pound, sold for less than 60 cents a pound. . . . Novocaine that sold for $1,600.00 a pound to the dentists is selling at the present time for $25.00 a pound to the people who supply the dentists; and I could mention many other similar substances.

The upshot of the long campaign was the passage and signing, in 1922, of the Fordney-McCumber Tariff Law. It is more than a coincidence that real recovery from the postwar chemical slump, at Midland and elsewhere, dates from this time. This was the first American tariff law ever to recognize the chemical industry as a national asset worth guarding and encouraging, and for the first time the industry became publicly known as a good place to invest money. Assured of fair "ground rules" for competition, manufacturers began making and bringing to market products that would have been too much of a gamble before. Nor did the real or pretended fear that the tariff would be used to keep prices high come to anything. In 1919, a depression year in the chemical business, aniline was selling at 24 cents a pound. By 1928, a boom year of high prices, aniline was selling at 14 cents. In the same period, monochlorbenzene went from 15 to 5 cents; magnesium went from $1.50 to 57½ cents. The process was typical: allowed to get really started and to compete on a fair basis, manufacturers rivaled one another in efficiency of production and marketing. As inevitably happens, this brought sales up, prices down, and led to the search for more and more useful products. This was just the atmosphere Herbert Dow liked to work in, and he now guided The Dow Chemical Company to some of the major achievements of modern industrial chemistry. Some of these were to stand complete in his lifetime; some were to reach full fruition only after his death. All were creative and useful achievements of which any company, industry, or country might well be proud.

17

REVOLUTION IN PHENOL

IN EXAMINING THE ACHIEVEMENTS OF A CHEMICAL MANUFACTURING COMPANY, there is always the danger that too much regard will be paid to "chemistry" and not enough to "manufacturing." Sometimes the "chemistry" is the more dramatic, as when a company actually invents a chemical that finds wide and striking use. This is especially true when the new chemical happens to be a brand-new dye, medicine, fabric, plastic or other product that catches the public fancy.

But gratifying as such spotlighted triumphs are, a large chemical company could scarcely hope to live by them alone. They happen too rarely, and behind them are only too often a great many years and millions of dollars laid out in research. Large chemical companies, then, must live by producing more and more skillfully vast quantities of chemicals of which the public seldom hears. These are often such "work horse" items as chlorine and caustic soda and sulfuric acid and so on, which are used to make still other chemicals. These "work horses" may do their job within the company's gates, or they may be sold to perform elsewhere, or some may be used in the plant and some sold. In any event, the company's financial success may well depend on its skill at producing these unpicturesque items, for here minute fractions of a penny a pound or a gallon are of utmost importance, because of the great quantities involved.

Something now happened at Midland which illustrates all the above points very well. The Dow Chemical Company developed a method, still unexcelled, for producing cheap phenol. Some of the chemistry concerned had been known for years: it had in fact been described in textbooks, usually with the warning that it could not be made to work in the factory. The Dow contribution was to *make* it work in the factory—work so well that the company became, and has remained ever since, the world's chief single producer of what is now one of the most useful of chemicals.

The last that the reader heard of phenol, the stuff was a complete drug on the market. There were millions of unwanted pounds stored all over the country, four million pounds at Midland alone. That was in 1918, when few chemical manufacturers expected ever to make another pound of phenol. Yet by 1923, when Dow began making phenol by the "unworkable" process, the chemical was in tremendous demand, and the company had brought about what is still one of the most productive triumphs of American chemical engineering.

Phenol is a colorless crystalline solid. Though used today by the millions of tons, few persons outside of chemical or related plants have ever seen it. Most people of middle age or more have at least smelled it, though. Carbolic acid, whose antiseptic and pungent reek used to feature hospitals, sickrooms, and doctors' offices, is more than 98 per cent phenol. In fact, when a professional chemist isn't listening too alertly, it is all right to speak of phenol as carbolic acid in solid form.

Up to the time of the first World War, about one million pounds of phenol were used a year in this country. A large part of it served, in the form of carbolic acid, as a general antiseptic. The rest went into Bakelite, a pioneer plastic invented by Dr. Leo H. Baekeland in 1907, and put on the market in 1909.

All of this phenol was "natural" and practically all of it was imported, chiefly from England. Phenol is one of the by-products which come off when coal is "coked" or "distilled"—that is, heated until it becomes coke. The coking of coal is one of the oldest of English industrial arts, partly because there was so much coal available. Originally, only two products of the coking process were of commercial interest. One was of course the coke: it was used in making steel, and as a home and industrial fuel. The other product was the gas that came off in the process: it was used for lighting, heating, and cooking. A third product, a tarry residue that drops out of the gas as it cools, was at first of small interest: it was practically given away to be smeared on roofs and roads. In time, however, it became apparent that this tarry residue was a chemical gold mine, rich in hydrocarbons from which dozens of dyes, medicinals, and other products could be made.[1]

[1] Hence the generic name "coal-tar products" still sometimes applied to such chemicals though the hydrocarbons in them may be synthetic. There is not enough coal tar produced in the world today to make more than a small fraction of the "coal-tar products" that are made and sold.

One of the first constituents of this residue to be deliberately recovered was phenol. The yield was not large—about a pint per ton of coal. Even so, the coke works of Europe, and especially of England, were able to supply Europe with all the phenol needed, with plenty left over for fairly cheap sale in the United States. Hence there had never been any great urge in this country to recover phenol from coal tar, especially as this would involve a complicated and expensive system of pipes, valves, tanks, condensers, and so on. Besides, we were still more of an agricultural nation than is generally remembered, and much more willing than we are today to rely on foreign factories for raw or semifinished materials.[2]

As the reader recalls, the outbreak of war in 1914 changed the whole phenol picture in the United States. Both the English and French had built their military "disruptive explosive" program around picric acid (trinitro phenol) as against the German choice of trinitro toluene or TNT. Almost at once the English and French found their sources of natural phenol critically inadequate, and asked American chemical plants to synthesize the chemical for them by the sulfonation of benzene. The process was already known, but considered too expensive to be commercially feasible as long as there was enough natural phenol around. The fact that chemical companies like Dow were able to meet the demand at all was in itself remarkable, and, for patriotic purposes, inspiring. However, from the point of view of the professional chemical engineer, with his preoccupation with problems of cost and efficiency, the feat left much to be desired. As Dr. Mark A. Putnam wrote in 1933: [3]

One of the first major organic chemical industries to develop as a direct result of the World War was the manufacture of synthetic phenol. At first, the problem was to get phenol quickly at any price. Plants were hastily thrown together; as many as fifteen were in operation at one time. However, as it became evident that the war was to have considerable duration, plants were rebuilt with greater efficiency and with more regard for chemical engineering principles. Among the

[2] Here was where men like Herbert Dow, in many industries besides the chemical, rendered this country more service than is ordinarily realized. They saw it was not enough for an industry to develop skill in making *finished* products: as long as *ingredients* for those products *had* to be bought abroad, control of the finished product could be exercised from abroad. A perhaps oversimplified instance of this, yet one which millions of motorists will recall with a twinge, was what happened when American tire manufacturers, who are certainly among the world's ablest, were cut off from their supplies of crude rubber in the last war.

[3] *Twenty-Five years of Chemical Engineering Progress* (American Institute of Chemical Engineers), pp. 26-27.

organizations which entered this field was that of Thomas A. Edison, which succeeded in manufacturing some product, and in getting a glowing write-up of its achievement in the *American Magazine*. However, the game was too stiff, and regardless of the unlimited demand for phenol at tremendous prices this plant was unable to continue.

As the war progressed and the prices more nearly approached reason, the weaker and less experienced firms dropped out. The total production at one time exceeded 320,000 pounds per day, which was a tremendous quantity of a difficult synthetic material to be produced by an industry less than three years of age. These plants were fairly well designed and operated with a reasonable degree of efficiency. This development made possible the manufacture on a very large scale of picric acid which was one of the most important high explosives used by the Allies and was an important factor in winning the war. After the Armistice, these plants stopped production, leaving the country with such an enormous stock of phenol that everyone lost interest in its further production.

Even at the close of the World War, however, the problem of manufacturing really cheap phenol had not been solved. Generally the problems of mass production and low costs are solved simultaneously. In this case, however, due to war conditions, low costs followed to some extent but did not keep pace with increased production.

For several years after the Armistice, the cost of producing phenol remained a matter of only academic interest, if any. Then, out of the blue, came a sudden rise in the manufacture of automobiles and of electrical equipment of one sort or another. Bakelite, a plastic made by reacting phenol with formaldehyde, came in tremendous demand for light parts and as an electrical insulating material.[4] Stocks of phenol left from the war were soon used up. At Midland the question arose: *Is it worth our while to get back into the manufacture of synthetic phenol?*

At the time, this was not an easy question to answer. There had already been one boom in phenol; it had, in a commercial sense, ended unhappily. This second one might well end the same way. There was no guarantee that the new demand for Bakelite would continue; the increase in automobiles and electrical equipment might be a flash in the pan, or some better and cheaper plastic might take Bakelite's job. Besides, it was known that three very large organizations, including the Bakelite Corporation itself, planned to go heavily into the manufacture of synthetic phenol. All three planned to use the sulfonation-of-benzene process, with such improvements

---

[4] This was, in a way, the real start of the astounding growth of the plastics industry. Celluloid was the first of the large-scale plastics and Bakelite the second. Now there are dozens, prominent among them a number of "phenolic plastics."

as each could think up. This meant that competition for the market, at least among these three, would be based on improving an already known process—a procedure that seemed to have reached its limit toward the close of the war.

In cases like this, the competition was not of a type that appealed strongly to Herbert Dow's business sense. Where he had a choice, he much preferred to compete by developing some new process that would from the start be better than what his rivals had, and keep improving his new process in order to maintain or even increase his lead. That way, if he won the race, he stood to win by yards instead of by inches. With this attitude in mind, Dow decided in 1922 to enter the phenol race.

As early as 1915, Herbert Dow had been discontented with the process of making phenol by starting out with the reaction of benzene and sulfuric acid. For one thing, the process involved a series of difficult steps. A more important charge against the process, in Dow's mind, was that it called for sulfuric acid. In those days, running a chemical plant without using oceans of sulfuric acid was just about unthinkable—except to Herbert Dow. In fact, he might be said to have made a career of avoiding the use of sulfuric acid. The reason for this was simple: sulfuric acid was not a logical product from his brine. If he were going to use sulfuric acid, he would have either to buy it from some other manufacturer, or buy ingredients to make it himself. This sort of thing never appealed to Herbert Dow: he was forever thinking in terms of his brine and what he could get out of it, in preference to other chemicals he could make or buy. In June of 1915, then, he had Dr. Strosacker and Robert Dreisbach work on a project of using brombenzol as a starting material; the "brom" of course to come from Dow brine. The project was laid aside, even after materials to build a plant had been ordered, when bromine prices rose so high that bromine was out of the question as a starting material.

In 1922, however, the idea was revived, this time with chlorbenzene; with the "chlor" coming from Dow brine. Drs. William J. Hale, Edgar C. Britton, and William H. Williams found that phenol could be produced with three very cheap Dow-made starting materials: chlorbenzol, caustic soda, and hydrochloric acid. Actually, this part of the work was not so much a discovery as a verification; the fact that these three cheap chemicals could make phenol had already been set down on paper, both in Germany and in England. But no one had yet made the process work commercially, because of the apparently insuperable chemical engineering problems in-

The "Automobile Age" offered Dow outlets for two of his pet products: magnesium alloys and bromine. Magnesium pistons did very well for a while and then fell by the wayside. Bromine in the form of ethylene dibromide for leaded gasoline eventually became and still is one of Dow's most important products. In the beginning, the antiknock fluid was mixed into the gasoline at the retail pump.

Magnesium manufacturing in 1930. The electric cables seen on the left are conducting current to the tall graphite electrodes, which in turn reach down into a large steel pot under the floor. The pot contains fused magnesium chloride which the current is separating into chlorine gas and metallic magnesium. The plant operator is ladling molten magnesium from the "hearth" at the front of a cell into forms in which it will quickly harden to billets like those shown. Today all Dow magnesium is manufactured from sea water in Texas, and sent to Midland and other plants for alloying and fabricating. The magnesium content of Midland brines is left in such compounds as Epsom salts, milk of magnesia, and magnesium chloride and oxychloride.

volved. Here was the perfect example of the situation that is forever confronting industrial chemists: a process that works nicely on paper may go all to pieces (or not go at all) when set up in the factory.

Hearing that a process he wanted to work wouldn't was usually enough to get Herbert Dow in one of his insistent moods, and that happened now. If they could make phenol from brombenzol they could make it from chlorbenzol too. Herbert Dow turned over the experimental notes from the 1915 brombenzol process to a young organic chemist, William H. Williams, with orders to do just that. After months of frustrations, half answers, and disappointments, the squad of chemists working on the problem came up with what looked like a successful process—on an experimental scale. But it remained to engineer this into a commercial plant. This meant, among other things, designing and building apparatus capable of handling efficiently the heat and pressure at which the reaction was to take place. Up to this time, most of the chemical reactions conducted in factories occurred at ordinary atmospheric pressure or, at most, at pressures of a few hundred pounds per square inch. Reacting chlorbenzol and caustic soda, however, required apparatus that could safely contain four or five *thousand* pounds of pressure per square inch, and standard equipment to handle such pressures did not exist. This difficulty was solved by having the reaction take place in very thick iron tubes of very small bore. There was also the matter of heat: how were the starting materials to be got efficiently and economically to a temperature of around 370° C., the temperature at which they react best? Dr. Mark E. Putnam finally solved this by the ingenious device of enclosing the reactor tubes within larger tubes through which the starting materials entered. The enclosed reactor tube was hot from the reaction going on within it; the starting materials, in flowing around it, picked up enough heat to be ready to react as soon as they entered the smaller tube. This "exothermal" procedure worked so well that a small flame provided all the heat needed to keep the process moving.[5]

---

[5] Nowadays it is possible to buy much of the equipment to do such jobs. In those days it was not: it was a question of devising and building the equipment in the Dow plant, or abandoning hope of being able to handle the process. There was, of course, also the alternative of waiting around till some equipment manufacturer devised and built the equipment. Herbert Dow seldom waited around for something he was convinced his own company could do, and this attitude led to some of the company's most striking achievements. It also led to some lively discussions as to whether he was primarily interested in chemistry, engineering, thermodynamics, research, or invention. The fact is that he was interested in all of these activities at once, and above all in teaming them to produce chemicals.

All this had made the process mechanically possible—a thing which several important textbooks of the day said it could not be. Now remained the task of making it really efficient commercially. This brought up the second set of problems: what to do with the chemicals the process produced besides phenol. It is characteristic of chemical processes that they seldom produce just the product you want: they almost invariably produce it and something else. Very often the commercial success or failure of the process depends on whether you find some productive use for the something else.

In the case of the new phenol process, there were four "something elses." One was salt. This was sent back to the chlorine-caustic cells, which broke it up into caustic soda, hydrogen, and chlorine. Bearing in mind that the starting materials for the phenol process are caustic soda, chlorbenzol, and hydrochloric acid, we see that the by-produced salt helps supply the caustic soda and, through the chlorine, the chlorbenzol and hydrochloric acid.

Two other by-products of the process are orthophenylphenol and paraphenylphenol. These chemicals are peculiar to Dow, and important markets for both have been developed. Each is the basis of a series of the famous Dowicides, which are chemicals used by various industries to kill fungi or bacteria in wood, paper pulp, glue, rope, yarn, fabrics, and so on. Paraphenylphenol is also the basis of a marine varnish which minimizes friction and enables the hulls of vessels to slip easily through the water. The varnish has performed this function for vessels ranging from the yachts raced by Commodore Vanderbilt against the late Sir Thomas Lipton to the swift PT boats of the recent war.

The fourth and in a way most interesting by-product of the process is diphenyl oxide. Diphenyl oxide smells like geraniums and goes in quantity to manufacturers of soaps, perfumes, and other toilet goods. Still more of it is made into Dowtherm, a liquid used as a high temperature, low pressure "heat-transfer agent" in many industries. As in the case of orthophenylphenol and paraphenylphenol, sales of diphenyl oxide help pay for the phenol process (and vice versa), thus lowering costs all around.

However, not all the diphenyl oxide *normally* produced in the phenol process can be sold; the market for it just isn't that big. Inasmuch as this normal production runs around one eighth to one ninth of final product, this could have turned out to be a serious storage and inventory problem. Instead, it stimulated the Dow team to an interesting and valuable discovery. It was found that if this one eighth to one ninth of diphenyl oxide was added to the starting materials at the *beginning* of the process, *no more diphenyl oxide was formed during the process.* The commercial value of this discovery is obvious. When diphenyl oxide is wanted, none is put in at the start; when it is not wanted, it is recycled over and over through the process. Thus the supply of diphenyl oxide for sale can be turned off and on at will—a thing which chemical engineers (and sales departments) devoutly wish could be done with a lot of other by-products.

So, starting out as a gamble, Dow's "impossible" phenol process became, technically and economically, one of the happiest marriages yet seen on this earth between chemistry and engineering. Naturally, the process did not spring into full flower overnight: for years improvements were being worked up and added. Nevertheless by 1923, little more than a year after the decision to resume making phenol, the process was producing well enough to make Dow a major figure in the country's phenol production. This position the company has never relinquished. Today about half the country's output of hundreds of millions of pounds a year comes from Midland. Much of it goes to manufacturers of phenolic plastics and other products. The rest is used at Midland to make dozens upon dozens of Dow chemicals, notably aspirin and the salicylates. Some of these phenol-based products became part of the Dow line in Herbert Dow's lifetime and some afterwards; in either case the company's pre-eminence in the field stems directly from Herbert Dow's insistence that an "unworkable" process could be made to work.

Incidentally, the Dow phenol accomplishment provided a curious foot-note to Herbert Dow's bromine war with the Germans of some years be-fore. In those days they had tried contemptuously to crush him as an upstart; yet under Hitler even the proud I. G. Farben appropriated and operated the Dow phenol process along with their own. In time they got to feeling so happy about the "borrowed" process that their textbooks and technical literature began to speak of it quite openly as "the Dow process." Had he lived to see it, this might have given Herbert Dow a laugh. But he was always challenging processes described in textbooks, and this might have inspired him to set his team off on a hunt for a still better phenol process.

18

HERBERT DOW AS INDUSTRIAL PHILOSOPHER

THERE IS A PITFALL IN EXAMINING THE CAREERS OF SUCCESSFUL INDUSTRIALISTS like Herbert Dow. Their very success makes us tend to regard them only as *doers,* and not also as *thinkers.* Or, granting they do think, we assume this is almost entirely along lines of their specific and immediate business problems.

There may be industrialists like that, but Herbert Dow was not one of them. People who knew him well recall that his mind was always "going"— and by no means all the time about his own plant or even about chemistry. The purpose of this brief chapter is to step aside from the story of his achievements for a few pages and report, in his own words wherever possible, some of his ideas about life and industry in general.

He saw, for instance, a direct cause-and-effect relationship between advance in ability to convert power and the advance of civilization. In 1926 he wrote to a friend:

We have recently been building a new power plant here, and some thoughts in connection with the use of power may interest you. Apparently all civilizations have been based on power. By power I mean foot pounds or actual ability to lift weight, as indicated by horsepower or kilowatts. But the power of the early civilizations was slave power, and when one nation conquered another and increased their number of slaves, they correspondingly increased their power and their civilization. Genghis Khan and his hordes who came down from Siberia and conquered Eastern Europe also depended to a considerable extent on horsepower from horses; but all these civilizations came and went in accordance with the ability of the victors to hold a greater or lesser number of human beings in slavery.

About the time of the American Revolution, Watt invented a marked improvement in the steam engine which increased its economy several fold and for the first time made the consumption of coal per horsepower small enough so that it became a real factor in competition with the power of horses or men, and from that date on our civilization was on a distinctly different basis from any previous civilization.

In that connection, Dow was fond of pointing out how modern industrial methods, in competition with one another, had given people more things to enjoy and more leisure to enjoy them in. Industrial literature has of late made that point so often that it has become a sort of abstract platitude that people shrink from hearing again. Dow had however actually lived through the transition from long hours and few luxuries to short hours and many luxuries; it is therefore perhaps interesting to hear how the change had struck him at first hand. He once wrote to Joseph W. Naramore, a boyhood friend who had become a clergyman:

When we were boys in Derby the average man worked sixty hours per week and was able to provide the necessities and some comforts and luxuries for his family. When my father was a boy a carpenter worked from sunrise to sunset and they had rather less comforts than we had. At the present time, when almost everyone has an expensive automobile and other luxuries that were not dreamed of when we were boys, the average man need work only 44 or 48 hours a week in order to secure these added comforts. It is improved automatic machinery that has made it possible for people at the present time to get so much more for fewer hours of work, and as the use of automatic machinery increases, it is going to be possible for people to enjoy more and more comforts or work less and less hours, or a combination of the two.

If, however, some *artificial* arrangement increases prices or decreases hours of work, the average man of necessity must enjoy less of these products. Or if one industry makes an abnormal profit, then everyone else has to pay the bill, and that one particular industry that receives the excessive profits apparently prospers. But I am sure that in the long run any artificial combination that restricts output or raises prices is ultimately detrimental for the consuming public, although it may be apparently beneficial for the immediate recipients of the extra profits. . . .

As we know, Dow's life work as a manufacturer coincided with the rise in American industry of really effective mass production.[1] As the public became more and more aware of the magic of mass production as against the old methods, it began to assume that all a man need do to make a fortune was set up a factory and mass-produce in it. No one knew better than Herbert Dow that success is by no means automatically assured, for mass production methods compete with each other every bit as vehemently as the old methods do. As early as 1919 he pointed out:

[1] In general, the chemical version of mass production is the large-scale continuous process, automatically controlled wherever possible.

In our Midland plant we have one vacuum pan that will turn out more than 100 tons per day of product, and it can be operated by one man. If we are in competition with another plant equally situated in other ways except that the capacity of the pan is only 10 or 20 tons per day, then we have a decided advantage. If, however, some competitor had a pan that would turn out 100 tons per day with a smaller consumption of steam than we used, he would have the advantage, other things being equal. If the market would not take the product of both factories, then we would have to close down and quit or find a way of beating him.

The Dow Company has been most successful in meeting competition through designing new and more up-to-date methods than its competitors. Just as no amount of cutting of wages of women who did sewing by hand would ever make it possible for hand labor to compete with the sewing machine, in a similar way no cut of wages will ever make it possible for a chemical plant using antiquated methods to compete with a plant using superior processes.

This awareness by Herbert Dow of the realities of competition led to an apparent anomaly. By 1928 his plant was making more than a hundred products, many of them "firsts." But conspicuous by their absence from the Dow roster of products were many for which there was wide sale and presumably promise of large profits.[2] Why wasn't Dow climbing aboard these band wagons? Didn't he know about them? Was he falling behind the times?

Apparently by 1928 such questions were worrying more and more stockholders, and in his annual report of that year he explained his policy. Because his statement gives so much of his philosophy of making and selling, it is here reproduced pretty much in full:

It has never been the policy of the Dow Company to manufacture any product because some other chemical company was apparently making money out of that product. In fact, if another company was making money on a certain product, it was probably because it had special advantages, or was unusually skilled, or was in possession of valuable patents, or an unusually desirable location, or some other abnormally favorable factor. Because it was making money, it would be able to conduct research in order to enable it to gain on the lead it had already acquired. In many ways the first firm to make a success of any given line of manufacture has a distinct advantage.

The Dow Company started in Midland because it had an unusually good

[2] Synthetic dyes, for instance. There are hundreds of them, and Dow was the first in this country to synthesize one of the most difficult—indigo. Yet he chose (and The Dow Chemical Company still chooses) not to "go into the dye business," but to develop just the indigo and brom-indigo lines.

process for making bromine and Midland was an unusually good location where this process could be carried out. It has consistently worked on the development of the brine that is peculiar to this locality and has always pushed the development of products that were peculiarly its own.

If the newspapers and trade periodicals create a great wave of interest over a certain line of chemical development, it is almost certain that this line will be overdone. If we develop that same interest within our own plant for our own products, it will tend to create an enthusiasm for our products that will cause our processes to be more highly refined and better operated and ultimately more profitable.

Somewhat related to Herbert Dow's lack of interest in already established products was his wariness of too much already established information. This was especially true if that information was practically the only tool in a man's intellectual kit. He once wrote to a chemistry professor at the University of Michigan, which incidentally has long rivaled Case School as a source of supply of Dow chemists and engineers:

When a chemical engineering course is made very stiff, as I have no doubt yours is, it makes it possible for a certain type of man to graduate with honors who can acquire ideas from others and from words, and it is questionable in my mind if the extreme proficiency attained in acquiring ideas from words does not to some extent detract from the ability to acquire ideas by contact with actual phenomena rather than words. I realize that your laboratory work overcomes this handicap to some extent, and may overcome it to the greatest extent that is possible in an educational institution. Please pardon my continual harping on this subject.[3]

Especially in his last years, Dow wrote a great many letters explaining his theories of management. Typical is this letter to Dr. W. R. Veazey, then professor of chemistry at Case School:

I have intuitively acquired a number of ideas, possibly they may be prejudices, that relate to methods of running a manufacturing plant. As you are interested in the general subject of efficient operation of The Dow Chemical Company, I will give you some of these views.

When The Dow Chemical Company was organized I made the remark to Mr. Convers that I did not think we needed much of an office. He immediately complimented me on this viewpoint, and I think nobody doubts Mr. Convers' ability as a manufacturer. He won out manufacturing tacks, which was an old competi-

[3] It was in this connection that Dow used to complain occasionally, "The schools don't turn out men like Barstow and Strosacker any more." There is not an overproduction of men like Herbert Dow, either.

tive line and therefore an especially hard one for a man to make a fortune out of.[4]

I am no believer in an engineer having an oiler. He no sooner gets this oiler than he sits down and the oiler becomes the man who is in intimate contact with his job and therefore knows his engine and the engineer proceeds to be the equivalent of a man sitting in the office.

When they put the addition on the power house they had a room with all the control instruments in it; all the records appeared there and they proceeded to operate the power house from this little office, called the control room. I objected to it because the men would control the machines that they were not in intimate contact with, which constitutes another phase of the tendency everywhere of fellows to migrate to an office with a desk and easy chair, but I was not sure enough of my position to arbitrarily head it off. It has been on my mind ever since and I cannot help thinking it is a bad idea for the engineers to have an office and desk from which they can control their equipment and issue orders without themselves being in as intimate contact with the subject as it is possible for them to be.

The same arrangement has been contemplated for the new power house and a room provided for this purpose; but I have just headed it off and I think it is going to be a big step in keeping the engineer in contact with his machinery instead of his office chair.

I would bank my whole reputation as a plant manufacturer on the fundamental basic idea that wherever possible keep a man in as close contact with his job as possible.

This was a favorite subject with Herbert Dow, and a few days after the above letter he was writing:

What I am emphasizing is the fact that a man cannot intelligently control anything without being in intimate contact with it. You remark that there is a tendency to multiply helpers and use the higher-up men in emergencies. My comment is that the helper is more competent to straighten things out in an emergency than the man higher up is unless the higher-up has had the experience of being a helper. My idea of a big man is one who after he is in touch with a small

[4] The reader will recall that Mr. Convers was president of The Dow Chemical Company from the beginning till 1918, and chairman of the board from then until his death in 1935. He had made his fortune in tacks by a curious strategy. Tacks were a simple mass-production item, and the only way to stand out in the field was to produce considerably faster than the competition. This looked like an impossible thing to do, because all the manufacturers used standard machines that would run only so fast without chronically breaking down. Mr. Convers deliberately ran his machines so fast that they did break down, found out in this way what parts usually broke, and had those parts privately redesigned so they wouldn't break. Presently he had a battery of tack machines that could run faster than anyone else's, and in that way moved to the head of the field.

job, then becomes acquainted with another small job, and another, and another, until he knows the game. I am surprised every few days at the incompetency of men, due to the fact that they do not know what many men under them know perfectly.

Dow set forth the above theories of management toward the close of his life. His plant was making some one hundred fifty products and sales were running around $17,500,000 a year. Today there are many hundreds of products, sales are in the hundreds of millions a year, and there are huge plants in various parts of the country. Obviously, the company's life is now many times more complicated than it was in Herbert Dow's day, and he would be the first to admit that today a lot of executives have to stay close to their desks and control panels whether they want to or not. Still, a surprising number of top men at The Dow Chemical Company are even today more apt to be found in the plant than in their offices, and many a high official could at a moment's notice take over and run the factory processes for which he is responsible as deftly as the foreman on the job.

The fact is that by 1930, when Herbert Dow died, the company had already become so large and so variegated in activity that it was getting more and more impossible to expect any one man to "know all the answers and run the whole show." This is a point that companies that started out and grew as his did always reach sooner or later. And it is a very critical point in such a company's history, for the company's very survival is then at stake. It is at this point that small companies have been known to fall apart, or be taken over by larger concerns, or become "efficiently organized" to the extent that individual imagination and drive and enterprise are quashed. The way the company has continued to grow since Herbert Dow's death, even during the years of depression which killed off so many companies, shows how well these pitfalls of growth were perceived and avoided.

There is, by the way, a very good reason why the management that has succeeded Herbert Dow was able to accomplish that all-important transition: he trained the men. And he had trained them, not in the stultifying obedience and protocol so highly prized in so many organizations, but in productive and unfeigned team spirit.

Herbert Dow loved to travel, and in his middle and late years he got around the world quite a bit. He went four times to Europe, twice each to the Caribbean and to Hawaii, and once to Japan. These were always family excursions, except that Dow put in a good deal of time noticing and philosophizing about how foreign industrialists did things. He noted that European automobile manufacturers were making wide use of magnesium—an intelligent move he never succeeded in getting American automobile manufacturers to make. In Japan, though he did visit some factories, he spent much of his time examining Japanese gardens. These much appealed to his fancy; and his own grounds and gardens, which remained his chief hobby his whole life, broke out in a rash of gnarled trees, curved bridges, bare rocks, and other Japanese features as a result.

He found Holland to be "the neatest place in the world," and much admired the industriousness of the Dutch in converting swamp into useful land. He was much impressed with the orderliness of the vast German forests, where the trees grow in rows as in an orchard, and not a twig falls to the ground without being noted and gathered. Germany, like several other nations of Europe, struck him as what he called a "finished" country— a country, that is, where much of the work has already been done; he thought this accounted for the periodic German urge to take over other countries and make a career of putting them in order, too. Of England he wrote:

A stranger arriving in England is at once impressed with the permanence of everything. Most of the houses are of stone, even the cheapest houses. Along the sea are great walls that were not built of concrete such as we use that has only been tested out for a decade or two, but these walls are made out of the rocks that have already stood the wear and tear of the ages. All the roads are stone roads, and if one would go from one of these roads bordering the sea down to the level of the beach, he would in most cases go down stone steps that were made of solid granite. The railroads, like the highways, are also very permanently constructed. They pass on massive stone arches over the country highways. They pass through the hills in stone-arched tunnels. These tunnels are only large enough to accommodate the size of cars that were common 25, 50 or 75 years ago, when these roads were built. To attempt now to use bigger locomotives than the tunnel clearance will permit or the heavy freight cars that we have in America, would entail such revolutionary changes as to make the change unthinkable. While the passenger cars are in some cases somewhat similar to our own and equally as comfortable, there is a very great difference in the freight cars, 6 or 8 tons being the ordinary capacity as against 40 or 50 tons in America. The impression an American gets in going through England is that it is a finished country; there is nothing begun and left half done.

Herbert Dow's travels, like anyone else's, were not without humorous incident. On one of his trips to England he had crossed on the *Mauretania* and been horribly seasick. He had a look at the ship's turbines and concluded they were the cause of the beam roll that made him uncomfortable. Later he wrote to a friend:

I had a letter of introduction to Sir Charles Parsons (the great English authority on turbines) and spent one evening with him at the Athenaeum Club in London. Got into an argument with him as to what made the Mauretania roll before I realized that it was propelled by Parsons turbines. I think I got less out of the meeting than I would otherwise have done.

On one of his Caribbean trips Dow came on a sight that was to haunt him in a humorous way for some years. All his life he had been a close student of the science of thermodynamics—the technique, that is, of converting fuel to power and getting the most out of the fuel and power. At a factory in the Caribbean he happened to see a massive stationary steam engine that seemed designed to be as inefficient as possible: so much energy went to moving the engine's cumbersome parts that little was left to do any work. Later on, back in Midland, it occurred to him that he would like to set this monstrosity up in his equipment-design department, as a warning how not to design. He instituted a search for the engine but it had vanished, and even the thousand dollar reward he put up for information leading to its apprehension never located it.

Before leaving the subject of Herbert Dow's philosophy as an industrialist, we should note once more that he was essentially a creator. His aim in business was to keep creating new products or better ways to make old ones. He did this himself and he inspired, bullied, badgered, and wheedled his team of devoted men into doing it. He was one of the first American industrial chemists to see that creation is the industry's big job, and to accept the business fact that creation costs time, money, and—perhaps above all— patience and courage in the face of frustration. Establishing this spirit in his own company, and helping establish it in the whole industry, may well have been Herbert Dow's chief contribution to his company and the industry.

19

DOW AND MAGNESIUM

I<small>N THE MINUTE BOOK OF THE</small> M<small>IDLAND</small> C<small>HEMICAL</small> C<small>OMPANY, THERE APPEARS</small> this entry for February 5, 1896:

Moved that Messrs. Cooper, Graves and Dow make experiments not to exceed $100 on method of making magnesium hydrate.

The motion was carried, and thus opened a chapter in American industrial chemistry that has not been excelled for stubbornness in the face of year-after-year frustration, or for importance of final outcome. As such it is worth examining in some detail.

As the reader recalls, the brine under Midland is fairly rich in five chemical elements: bromine, chlorine, sodium, calcium, and magnesium. There are of course also the hydrogen and oxygen which form the water in which the five elements appear in such compounds as sodium chloride, calcium chloride, magnesium chloride, and magnesium bromide. The basic aim of Herbert Dow's industrial life, and the only large-scale activity of the company till years after his death, was to get the various elements out of the brine and find uses and markets for them.

We have already reviewed at some length the success with four of the elements. Bromine was made into a wide range of bromides and brominated compounds. Chlorine served as an ingredient or as a processing material for dozens of chemicals. Sodium was exploited as caustic soda, one of the most widely used of the "work horse" chemicals. Calcium found vast tonnage markets as calcium chloride for refrigeration and roads. Only the fifth of the elements, magnesium, kept resisting Dow's efforts to find what he considered completely satisfactory markets for it.

Nothing came of the $100 research project which opened the struggle in 1896. For the next eighteen years, despite sporadic efforts to find some way to avoid doing it, the valuable magnesium content of the brine had to be thrown away as sludge. This pained Herbert Dow very much. He hated to throw things away, and he hated to feel there was in his possession something for which no use could be found. For some eighteen years then, magnesium sludge occupied the same position in Dow's mind that high society occupied in the mind of Ralph Waldo Emerson: it was not good enough to keep, but too good to throw away.

The first break in the situation came just as the first World War was beginning in 1914. What magnesium compounds were used in this country had always come mostly from Germany, which had copious and easily available magnesium deposits at Stassfurt. By a fortunate coincidence, Dow had been getting set up to make these compounds to try to compete for the limited market just as the war broke out. With demand rising and German imports cut off by the British blockade, Dow was presently finding increasing amounts of the magnesium content of his brine going into four standard magnesium products. One of these was magnesium sulfate, the familiar Epsom salts of the drugstore and of industry. Another was magnesium hydrate, familiar as milk of magnesia and as an intermediate in the production of Epsom salts. The other two were magnesium oxychloride, for flooring and stucco, and magnesium chloride, used in cement, and as a starting material for other magnesium products, including magnesium metal.

The demand for these products survived the war, but still didn't satisfy Herbert Dow. As he saw it, the really expansive future of the magnesium content of his brine lay in magnesium metal. Use of the compounds, he felt, might increase in volume but not much in kind, and limitation of the kind of uses would always be standing by to limit eventual volume. On the other hand, he felt, magnesium metal, like chlorine, might develop so many uses that demand for it would be limitless. It was to this last proposition that he was to devote so much time, energy, and money during the last ten years of his life. Almost alone among Americans, he, a chemist, was to campaign to establish magnesium as a useful metal.

During the first World War, Herbert Dow's interest in magnesium metal was exactly the same as the interest of the four or five other companies which also undertook to produce it. Pure magnesium, when powdered, burns very readily and with an extremely intense white light. Its chief use, till the outbreak of the war, was in fireworks and as a flashlight powder in photography. The war brought it into great temporary demand for tracer bullets and for star shells to light up night combat. In fact, military demand for the metal became so great, and the difficulties of making it were so many and so unexplored, that American-made magnesium brought as much as five dollars a pound. Like the several other American manufacturers who tried it, Dow learned to make magnesium metal during the war. But production methods were crude and expensive: their one merit, and at the time the only merit that counted, was that they made magnesium at all.[1]

At the war's end the demand for American-made magnesium dropped to practically nothing. The chief reason for this was that this country did not accept magnesium as a *structural metal*—a metal, that is, of which metal objects and parts could be made. Aluminum had established itself as *the* light metal, and it was to aluminum that the manufacturers of metal objects and parts automatically turned when they wanted a very light metal. This was in spite of the obvious fact that magnesium is *one third lighter than aluminum*.

There were two other very real reasons why consumers of metal were not interested in magnesium. One was cost. Techniques of making the metal were still in their infancy in this country, and therefore inevitably expensive. The cost of manufacturing a new product is usually lowered only by the simultaneous operation of two factors: improved production technique and volume sales. The two interlock because almost always the aim of improving production technique is to increase volume; if this increased volume meets no market, improvement has been in vain, at least in the commercial sense.

Magnesium's other handicap as a metal was that there was in this country no body of knowledge of how to "work" it. The metal industry had been working for centuries with iron, steel, copper, tin and so on. Even aluminum, the newest of the structural metals, had been worked in factories for some forty years. Of the traditional metals, there was wide (though still incomplete) knowledge of alloys, melting points, coefficients of thermal expansion, tensile and yield strengths, and so on; a great deal was also known about how to forge, cast, roll, or extrude the familiar metals. Practically none of these things was known of magnesium in this country, and no user of metal was willing to spend the time and money required to discover them.

---

[1] The technical difficulties will not be gone into here, but there was great rejoicing in Midland when the first piece of magnesium metal, about the size of a dollar watch, was produced in the laboratory and put on proud display in the window of Bert Carter's drygoods store on Main Street. A few months later, in July of 1916, a chunk of magnesium weighing one hundred pounds was made.

What it boiled down to, then, was this. Any American manufacturer who hoped to make money making and selling metallic magnesium had four very big jobs on his hands:

1. He must learn to manufacture the metal cheaply, so that it could compete in price with the traditional metals.
2. He must convince users of metal that they should use magnesium.
3. He must either discover and tell customers how to work the metal, or else work it for them. Inasmuch as unalloyed magnesium is worthless as a structural metal, this involved inventing a line of magnesium alloys and devising proper techniques for working each one.
4. He must do the above jobs in competition with the powerful German Chlormagnesium Syndikat, or Magnesium Trust, which since 1907 had been working with magnesium, had already developed and patented a number of very good magnesium alloys, and knew how to fabricate them.[2]

The remarkable thing is not that Herbert Dow, although a chemist and not a metallurgist, undertook to attempt the fourfold job. The remarkable thing is that he did not bow out of the job when its complication and magnitude became clear, and it began its annual practice of costing the company hundreds of thousands of dollars a year. It was this doggedness, which to some of his sincerest supporters often looked like stubbornly throwing good money after bad, that gave our country its independence in the matter of magnesium, and may in fact have saved its life in the recent war.

As so often happens with a proposed new product, Dow's magnesium adventure started off with all the earmarks of a gamble with pretty good chances of turning out well. What seemed to be the major production problem was soon solved. For some time it had been known that magnesium metal could be obtained by electrolyzing magnesium chloride into magnesium and chlorine. This much was achieved in various sizes, shapes, and kinds of experimental cell. However, the metal was always in the form of pea-sized globules which slithered around on top of the molten liquid as elusively as globules of mercury on a glass-topped desk. It became a tantalizing problem to get these globules to come together; and it was at this time that Herbert Dow often remarked he'd like to see a pound of

---

[2] The creating of magnesium metal and its alloys is spoken of as *manufacturing* magnesium; working the metal into forms and shapes is called *fabricating*. Dow was hoping that if he manufactured the metal, customers would come forward and fabricate it. It didn't turn out that way: he had to do both.

magnesium in one piece, instead of in the form of a handful of buckshot. When, in the middle of 1916, a solid hundred-pound chunk was obtained, Herbert Dow was all eagerness to set up a manufacturing plant.

This involved, of course, the customary tussle with the board of directors. The company treasury was already low, and he had just taken a big bite out of it to set up an expensive indigo plant that might or might not make indigo and money. A plant for making metallic magnesium looked like even more of a commercial gamble. The peacetime market was small and the Germans had traditionally supplied it. They would surely be back after the war. It would then be a question of competing not only with them, but with other American manufacturers; this promised a great deal of competition for a very small market. The directors were unenthusiastic but Herbert Dow was, as usual, adamant. They let him have $225,000 to set up a small magnesium plant.

As in the case of indigo, it was decided to try to go from the drafting board straight into full production, without first setting up a small pilot plant. The plant was in operation by January of 1917, and operated quite nicely for a couple of days. Then the molten magnesium chloride in the cells suddenly "froze" hard as granite and the building was as full of chlorine as a building can get. The cells were completely wrecked; the chlorine ate up the rest of the equipment and most of the building. The plant, in a word, junked itself; but in six months it was patched up and running again. Within a few more months the war, which had created the unusual demand for magnesium metal, was over. Dow kept on making it anyway, in the grim hope of finding a sizable market for it.

Meanwhile, with the war over, all the other American manufacturers but one dropped out at once. The one which remained was American Magnesium Corporation, a subsidiary of Aluminum Company. Aluminum had already been widely accepted as a light metal; even before the war, a hundred million pounds or so a year had been made and sold. Small amounts of magnesium are used to alloy aluminum; hence Aluminum Company's peacetime interest in it. It looked like a race between Dow and American Magnesium (and, of course, the German Magnesium Trust) to supply what little metallic magnesium there was a market for.

In February of 1920, a searing fire broke out in the little sixteen-cell magnesium plant, reducing it in a few minutes to a tangle of scrap iron. Nothing remained but twenty tons of stock-piled magnesium ingots.

Because the fire offered the company a graceful excuse to drop the whole

Sea-water intake for early Ethyl-Dow bromine plant at Wilmington, North Carolina. The plant opened in 1933, three years after Herbert Dow's death, though he had seen enough test runs before he died to know that his dream of getting bromine out of the ocean was commercially feasible. Today Ethyl-Dow operates a gigantic plant for this purpose in Texas.

Dow plant in 1930. Thirty years before, the plant consisted of a handful of buildings producing two products: bromides and bleach. Now it was producing over
800 carloads a month of about 150 products. Today, counting the output of Dow
plants outside Midland, dollar volume of output is about ten times as much.

complicated magnesium problem, it probably looked to a lot of people around Midland like a blessing in disguise. This view was not shared by Herbert Dow. Within a month the board of directors was voting:

RESOLVED: That the G. M.[3] be authorized to expend approx. $300,000 on buildings and equipment for the manufacture of mag.

While the new manufacturing plant was building, there was no letup in the project of devising magnesium alloys and methods of fabricating them. Magnesium metal for this, and for the very limited sales, came from the forty thousand pounds of ingots that had survived the fire; and they were more than enough to tide the men working on fabrication over until the new manufacturing plant was in operation. It was in this time that the company devised and produced the first of its eventually famous Dow-metals. These are alloys of magnesium suitable for structural use. There are today eleven of these Dowmetals in common use. All but one contain some aluminum; seven contain also zinc; one contains also tin; one contains also manganese. Some of these were perfected in Herbert Dow's lifetime and some afterwards; all involved long and costly trial-and-error experimentation and testing. The same was true of the work on fabrication techniques, which required costly machinery: there is no such thing as a small (or inexpensive) rolling or extrusion mill. Most of the fabrication techniques worked out in Herbert Dow's lifetime were for casting; rolling, forging, and extruding for the most part came later. Even so, the financial outlay for making and testing castings ran into a great deal of money, especially considering it was being laid out by a chemical rather than a metallurgical company.[4]

Despite the disappointing sales curve, Herbert Dow never relaxed his

---

[3] Dow was by now both president and general manager. Since the beginning he had been running the plant as general manager, and it was by that title that his colleagues usually thought of him. As already mentioned, Dow himself did not give a hoot for titles, chains of command, and other executive dignities: he just liked to see the work done.

[4] Herbert Dow repeatedly cut magnesium prices below what it cost him to make it, partly to stimulate sales and partly to stimulate his associates to find ways and means to produce it more cheaply. At one point, he cut the price to 72 cents a pound, which was less than the metal was costing him. A competitor who knew this was sure Dow was bluffing and ordered a carload, which was then a tremendous order. Dow sent the carload. The competitor, still unconvinced Dow was not bluffing, ordered a second carload. Dow sent that one, too.

enthusiasm for magnesium as the coming light metal. He was always sure that its universal acceptance was just ahead; at times he even envisioned magnesium's becoming The Dow Chemical Company's main product, with its massed chemicals playing a very much muted second fiddle. Typical of his all-out enthusiasm was his prediction in 1922 at a joint meeting of British, French, and American chemical societies:

We hope ere long to see magnesium rolling mills competing with steel mills and the world's lightest commercial metal find the place in the march of civilization that a product lighter and more abundant than iron deserves.

Meanwhile, two applications of magnesium metal which he very much supported came tantalizingly close to paying off in a big way. One was, curiously enough, in the very role in which Dow magnesium had so much to do with winning World War II. This was of course in aircraft. The planes of the day were still "box kite" affairs of wood, cloth, and wire; but aircraft manufacturers were thinking ahead to the modern all-metal plane. Magnesium being the lightest of structural metals, Dow's "magnesium team" was very much interested in what chance there would be here for magnesium. In May of 1919, Dr. Veazey wrote to Herbert Dow:

Mr. Robert J. Anderson, Metallurgist of the Bureau of Mines at Pittsburgh, called on me this afternoon and gave me the following information which I think is of vital importance to us. The United States Army has appointed an Aircraft Committee to investigate the production of complete metal aeroplanes. They propose to eliminate all wood and cloth. Some of the members of the committee propose the use of aluminum for this purpose but Anderson is convinced that Magnesium is well worthy of very careful consideration and trial. I have asked him to call on you in Midland Wednesday May 7 and discuss the matter with you and he has consented to do so.

I showed him a magnesium piston which Mr. Burdick sent me lately and he will have our pistons tried out in the Liberty motor if we will make them. He will of course furnish us the necessary specifications.

He says also that there are many other parts which may be made of magnesium if we can cast them. (Crankcase, exhaust manifold, instrument holders, carburetors, light duty bearings, etc.)

I think this is a rare opportunity for us to get a lot of testing done which if favorable will open up the field for magnesium better than anything else we can do. If successful on parts of the aeroplane it will certainly be adopted for similar parts on high class automobiles.

It was not till a decade later that the all-metal airplane became a reality. Aluminum, though half again as heavy as magnesium, became the favored metal for it. Herbert Dow had meanwhile seen which way the wind was blowing, and had devoted himself to trying to get magnesium into the planes in the form of propellers, motor parts, and so on. A hollow magnesium propeller was made at Midland and turned over to a propeller company, which adopted some of its design features but not magnesium. A few months before his death, in his 1930 annual report,[5] Herbert Dow was able for the first time to report progress made in his campaign to get magnesium into airplanes. There was, he reported, "greater activity than before in experimenting," and he added:

This spring for the first time three prominent airplane motors were shown at the Detroit aircraft exhibition with magnesium metal crankcases—namely the Packard, the Wasp and the Hornet.

Not much came of this small advance, however, and through most of the 1930's The Dow Chemical Company kept importuning the designers of civilian and military aircraft to make use of magnesium to save weight for useful load. These urgings were firmly ignored until after the Axis had begun its attack in 1939. Then it was discovered, by examining Axis planes that were shot down, that they owed a great deal of their speed and ability to carry heavy fuel supplies and bomb loads to weight savings through liberal use of magnesium parts.

The lesson sank in at last. The Dow Chemical Company was the only American concern which had never lost faith in magnesium and was ready to make it. The company had, in fact, just opened a big plant in Texas to get magnesium from sea water, and made large additions to its fabricating equipment. The company was now asked to manufacture and fabricate every ounce of magnesium it possibly could, and to show others how to manufacture and fabricate it. This second request, to which The Dow Chemical Company patriotically acceded, meant revealing to business rivals techniques and knowledge it had been twenty years patiently and expensively gathering. By the mid-point of the war, over 90 per cent of the millions of pounds of American-produced magnesium had come from Dow plants or plants which Dow personnel helped to set up. Today it is routine for aircraft, both military and civilian, to have many parts made of magnesium, and magnesium ranks high as a natural resource and as a critical defense material.

[5] The Dow fiscal year ends May 31.

ANOTHER USE FOR magnesium metal which Herbert Dow hoped to popularize did do very well for a while, and came close to becoming the volume outlet he was looking for. This use was in magnesium pistons for automobiles. These pistons move up and down many times a minute; their own weight adds to the power requirements to move them. Magnesium has only one sixth the weight of steel. Dow represented to automobile manufacturers that magnesium pistons would save a great deal of gasoline. But the automobile manufacturers were interested in the price of metal, not of gasoline, and magnesium did cost more than steel. Dow set up a plant to make magnesium pistons anyway, and was in production as early as 1919. In his annual report for 1921, he revealed with a mingling of enthusiasm and anticipation:

Dowmetal pistons were used in the eight-cylinder Frontenac car that won the great Indianapolis race a few weeks ago. Another Frontenac car equipped with Dowmetal pistons took third place. The most severe strain that can be put on an engine occurs in these races which take place annually in Indianapolis. The market for these pistons for use on Ford cars has increased very rapidly. We anticipate that it will reach such a point that it will tax our somewhat limited facilities to produce a sufficient quantity of these pistons to supply the demand. With our present facilities this will not be as large an industry as some of our other lines. Should the market grow, and should we build an additional plant to manufacture the metal, it may develop into a very large investment.

It turned out that neither Ford nor any other large manufacturer adopted Dowmetal pistons, but Herbert Dow managed to sell a great many anyway. Those were the days when after every few thousand miles a car's cylinders were usually rebored and its pistons replaced, and Dowmetal ones found a fairly receptive market as replacements. Then high-compression motors and better gasolines were developed, the replacement business fell off, and what had promised to be a volume market for magnesium metal vanished with it.

In 1927 the only other domestic manufacturer of the metal, American Magnesium Corporation, dropped out of manufacture but remained in fabrication, buying its raw metal from Dow. Actually, most of these purchases were used to alloy aluminum. The peak year of sales during Herbert Dow's lifetime was in 1929, when about 750,000 pounds were sold.

In the years immediately following World War II, annual sales of magnesium ran around forty to sixty times what they were in 1929, and sales are steadily rising. Some of this goes into aircraft, and into other applications where metal parts must be lifted or moved. Dowmetals are widely used for the bodies of trucks, trailers, and moving vans; their lightness makes more of the vehicle's gross weight available for "pay load." They find many uses in the textile industry, where machine parts move often and fast. They are used to make portable objects like ladders and wheelbarrows. They are used for electrodes which, buried in the ground near oil and natural gas pipelines, save many millions of dollars a year by cutting down corrosion. And as more and more uses are found, magnesium moves closer and closer to being what Herbert Dow insisted it would be—not only the lightest of metals, but also the most economical.

Herbert Dow predicted that his little magnesium plant would one day grow to overshadow everything he and the company accomplished in chemistry lumped together. This is a very tall order indeed, for it hands a single metal the job of trumping a lot of major achievements of the modern chemical industry. Actually, magnesium metal sales today constitute about 6 per cent of the company's total annual sales; vast tonnage sales of magnesium compounds like Epsom salt and magnesium oxide bring this percentage much higher. Thus Herbert Dow's vivid faith in magnesium not only finally provided the company an important source of income but helped win a war, and it gave this country a plentiful, economical, and purely American supply of the lightest structural metal there is.

As already noted, the Dow achievement in magnesium was the result of the courage and work of many men who shared his faith. To this statement should be added an observation by Willard Dow in a letter written in 1944:

I would like to call Dr. E. O. Barstow the "Father of Magnesium".... In many instances my father, being the executive head of the company at that time, naturally was given credit for his foresightedness and many other factors in the early days of magnesium, all of which were true. But the man who was actually responsible for its production and who brought it to a final conclusion was Dr. Barstow.

20

DOW MINES THE OCEAN

FOR THE FIRST THREE DECADES OF HIS CAREER, ONE OF THE CHRONIC PRE-occupations of Herbert Dow's days and nights had been to find quantity uses for bromine. Then in the fourth and last decade, the whole bromine picture turned end for end. From being a product hard to market in volume, it became one desired in such volume that even Herbert Dow wondered at first if the demand could be met. To him, to wonder about such a thing was to try. He tried, and the end result was perhaps the most spectacular achievement of his career. For it made his the first company to accomplish, on a continuing and commercial scale, what scientists had long been dreaming of doing: "mine" the ocean of some of its vast treasure of chemical content.

Most of us think of the ocean as just water and salt. The chemist, however, knows that down through the ages it has become a tremendous reservoir of a great many chemicals. Each cubic mile of ocean water contains, in fact, about 175,000,000 *tons* of assorted chemicals.[1] Provided expense is not a consideration, the chemist sees nothing remarkable about extracting any of these chemicals from ocean water. What Herbert Dow was now to lead, drive, inspire and badger a team of his men into doing was to get bromine out of the ocean with expense very much a consideration.

There are, on the average, sixty-seven parts of bromine in each one million parts of sea water. The problem was therefore to devise ways and means of taking in one million parts of sea water, stripping it of its sixty-seven parts of bromine, and disposing of the 999,933 parts of stripped water—and doing all this on a paying basis.

Before we look into how that was finally done, let's see what all this big

---

[1] Including gold, silver, copper, iron, potassium, aluminum, calcium, radium, strontium, sulfur, iodine, chlorine, sodium, magnesium, and bromine.

demand for bromine was about. Curiously enough, it was caused by the very thing which Herbert Dow had fruitlessly hoped would cause an all-out demand for magnesium—the mass-produced automobile.

During and after the first World War, automobiles and trucks had become fairly common in the United States, and the country was well on its way to its present "automotive mindedness." There was, however, one serious hitch in this development. This hitch was the gasoline: the better the car and truck motors became, the more unsatisfactorily the gasoline of the day worked in them.

The chief trouble was the "knock." The gasoline was supposed to explode in the cylinders with a firm surge of power. Instead, it went off with abrupt bangs that turned the crankshaft in a series of circular jerks which could be both heard and felt. This was rough on motor, passenger, and pocketbook. The pocketbook suffered in two ways. The driver was not getting his money's worth out of the gasoline, and he was forever having his motor repaired.

As early as 1916, the search was on for an answer to this. Presently it was clear what was needed: some inexpensive chemical to add to the gasoline to make it explode without the troublesome and uneconomical knock. Prominent in this search were the great Charles F. Kettering and the brilliant young Dr. Thomas Midgley, Jr., both of General Motors Research Laboratories. During six years of research, in which hundreds upon hundreds of chemicals were tried, three were found which would do the job.

The first to be found was iodine. This worked very well, but never got out of the laboratory. Iodine was then a foreign monopoly, and cost in this country around $4.50 a pound.[2] The second discovery was aniline: this worked fairly well, but not well enough. Then, late in 1922, the Kettering-Midgley team found a chemical that completely prevented knock. This was tetraethyl lead. In the laboratory and in test cars on the road it worked fine—for a while. Then it was found that the lead was gradually depositing itself in metallic form in cylinders, valves, and spark plugs, and eventually halting the engine. Thus the long-sought cure turned out to be worse than the disease.

A hunt was begun for a second chemical to add that would cause the lead to be discharged harmlessly into the atmosphere. It was presently found

---

[2] Herbert Dow was to lay the groundwork for breaking this monopoly by helping set up a company to get iodine from waste oil-field brines in Louisiana.

that ethylene dibromide was just the chemical for this job, and that a mixture of three fifths tetraethyl lead and two fifths ethylene dibromide made a very efficient antiknock fluid.

Ethylene dibromide was one of the ethylene compounds which Dow had known for years how to make, but for which he had been unable to find any appreciable market. Now, by a curious irony, almost everyone but himself and the men around him had serious doubts whether he or anyone else could supply enough bromine to make the amount of ethylene dibromide it was hoped would be needed when the antiknock fluid came on the market.

The Ethyl Gasoline Company was formed to make and market the new fluid, with Dr. Midgley at its head. He had adopted the use of bromine reluctantly, fearing, as he remarked, that "there isn't enough bromine in the world."

"We'll have to 'mine' it out of the ocean, then," Herbert Dow commented, and was thought to be joking.

The Dow Chemical Company had for years been this country's chief producer of bromine. It now contracted with Ethyl to deliver a steady flow of bromine for the next five years, increasing the flow if needed. Meanwhile, worried that even Dow might not be able to meet the demand expected, Ethyl began a world-wide search for additional sources. Included in this search were North Africa, the Dead Sea, and Herbert Dow's old acquaintance, the German Bromine Trust. North Africa and the Dead Sea proved not feasible and the Germans not enthusiastic.

Ethyl's next move was to set up, with the Du Pont company, a project to do the very thing Herbert Dow had hinted at—get bromine out of the ocean. A cargo steamer was bought, rechristened the S. S. *Ethyl,* and converted into a floating chemical plant. It spent March and April of 1925 at sea, actually taking bromine out of the ocean and combining it with a supply of aniline which it carried on board. The resultant chemical, tribrom aniline, was going to be substituted for the mixture of tetraethyl lead and ethylene dibromide as a complete antiknock agent in itself. But it was decided that sending a chemical plant to sea was not as good an idea as having the sea flow through a plant on the shore. It again became a question of being sure of enough bromine for ethylene dibromide.

Then, for a year or so, this question answered itself. There were some deaths from lead poisoning in the plant of the company that was making the tetraethyl lead. The conditions which caused this tragedy were corrected, but the lurid side of the press saw more to the story than met the eye. A hysterical newspaper campaign was begun against the use of leaded gasoline, however safely the lead part might be produced. Screaming headlines harped over and over on the unsettling theme that automobiles were discharging poisonous lead into the atmosphere, and that presently millions of people would die, after dramatic fits, of lead poisoning. All sale of leaded gasoline was stopped for a year, during which the United States Public Health Service investigated this frightful possibility—and found there was nothing to it.

Manufacture and sale of leaded gasoline—leaded with tetraethyl lead mixed with ethylene dibromide—were resumed in the middle of 1926. By then the boom of the twenties was on, the number of automobiles was increasing hand over fist, and the antiknock fluid was in great demand. On Dow fell the responsibility of supplying most of the ethylene dibromide for it, and Dow production of bromine was stepped up as never before. Additional brine wells were drilled at Midland. Dow had for some years owned brine wells at Mt. Pleasant, some thirty miles away. These were operated only in periods of unusual bromine demand, as in the first World War. In 1928 the Mt. Pleasant field was reopened and additional wells drilled. Ordinarily, the bromine obtained at Mt. Pleasant was shipped in the form of crude bromine to Midland; now a pipe line was constructed to bring the brine directly to Midland for bromine extraction. Additional wells were drilled on leased land along the route of the pipe line and their production of brine fed into it.

Thus, after years of crusading for markets for bromine, Dow was selling every pound of it he could make. But still he couldn't be sure of meeting the foreseeable demand. It was at this point, in 1928, that day-and-night pressure was begun at Midland to find an economical way of getting bromine out of the ocean.

It is sometimes supposed that the idea—and Herbert Dow's conviction that he could make it work—stemmed from the cruise of the *S. S. Ethyl* in 1925. But in July of 1924 he had written to J. S. Crider, one of the directors of The Dow Chemical Company:

. . . The "sewer" brine from the bromine plant normally contains about the same amount of bromine as the oceans. We have just made some tests to see how good an extraction we can get under extreme conditions and have been able to reduce the bromine down to a point where it is running 40% of the amount in the oceans. This would seem to indicate that we could extract bromine from the oceans, and recover 60% of the bromine in ocean water. However, bromine made in this way would not be cheap.

Now, with experimentation very much under way again, cost was still the central problem. As usual, Herbert Dow attacked the cost problem with his favorite weapon: technical skill of process combined with big-volume production. In April of 1928 he wrote to Professor A. H. White at the University of Michigan:

. . . If sometime in the future a real big demand for bromine arises, we will build a plant on the Atlantic Ocean or some other ocean, and take it out of ocean water. Normally our sewer in Midland contains the same amount of bromine that the ocean does, but as an experiment, we operated this plant with a sewer containing only one quarter as much bromine as there is in the ocean, so that we have a demonstration on a manufacturing scale and know how to apply it if necessary. However, the price of bromine extracted from the ocean would be higher than it is at the present time, unless the quantity should go into thousands of tons, in which case we might get an unprecedented low cost on account of the big scale of the operations.

With, then, the interrelated problems of efficient process and mass production in mind, tons upon tons of sea water from various points on the American coast were brought to Midland for experimentation. Before long it became clear what the chief chemical problem of getting bromine out of sea water economically was. Because of the almost infinitesimal amount of bromine in sea water, the use of electrolysis to free the bromine in such a dilute solution was economically out of the question. To free it by boiling out would be fantastically so. The bromine would have to be freed by the addition of acid and chlorine and then blown out. But a volume intake of sea water will keep varying slightly in what chemists call pH—that is, degree of alkalinity or acidity. Sea water is very slightly alkaline, but even that slight degree varies. If, during a period of variation, too little acid is added, there is a poor yield of bromine—and chlorine is wasted. If too much acid is added, there is a waste of acid. What it came down to, then, was finding an economical and sure-fire way to add just the right amount of acid and chlorine at any given moment. And, because of the tremendous volume of raw material being mined for such a small amount of product, these amounts of acid and chlorine had to be "right" to within a microscopic shading of accuracy.

For some time there had existed an instrument called a potentiometer, used almost exclusively in chemical laboratories, for accurately measuring pH or alkaline-acid status. What the Dow group now did was devise a potentiometer that would automatically keep measuring an intake of sea water, and automatically add to it the exact amount of acid and chlorine needed at any given moment. This solved the chief chemical problem: it guaranteed that, as far as chemistry alone was concerned, enough bromine would be recovered to make the process a paying proposition.

It remained now to engineer a plant that would actually do the job. A small pilot plant was set up at Midland. Herbert Dow was an almost daily visitor to its operation, which ran on into the autumn of 1930. A few weeks before his death, enough test runs had been completed to prove the process was a success. Thus he died not only believing that bromine could be taken out of the ocean on a commercial basis, but knowing it could—and knowing that his men could do it.

Meanwhile, a team of his chemists and engineers had been exploring the eastern and southern seacoasts for a suitable plant site. One was found at Kure Beach, in North Carolina. A plant was built which produced 500 pounds of bromine a day. Convinced now the job could be done, the Ethyl Company joined with Dow, on a fifty-fifty ownership basis, in setting up the Ethyl-Dow Chemical Company to produce ethylene dibromide. Production was increased to 15,000 pounds of bromine a day, and presently to 60,000.

Later the Kure Beach plant was closed and a much larger one put into operation at Freeport, Texas. There, day in and day out, millions of tons of sea water are stripped of their tiny content of bromine. The process is completely automatic and self-regulating—not a control is touched by human hands.

Incidentally, one of the outstanding engineering features of the plant is the adaptation of the "blowing out" tower of Herbert Dow's first days as an industrial chemist. One day a famous research chemist visited the plant and saw the tower in operation. He stared in surprise for a moment, then shook his head and made a remark that would have delighted Herbert Dow.

"Simple," he said. "Ridiculously simple. It doesn't do justice to research."

21

THE SUMMING UP

In 1924, in recognition of his achievements in industrial chemistry, Herbert Dow had been awarded an honorary degree of Doctor of Engineering by his alma mater, Case School of Applied Science. In 1929, he received a similar honor from the University of Michigan. Then in 1930, the last year of his life, he received the highest honor possible in American industrial chemistry, the Perkin Medal for Chemical Achievement. This award is the "Nobel Prize" of the chemical industry, and leaders of it from all over the country assembled at the Chemists' Club in New York to see Herbert Dow receive it.

Because so much of Dr. Dow's accomplishment stemmed from his personality and character, it was thought fitting to have James T. Pardee, an associate since their student days together at Case, speak at length of him as a person. This resulted in no mere hymn of praise from a friend: Mr. Pardee examined, with a businessman's detached acuteness, Dow's interest from boyhood on in "making things work"—and his refusal to accept frustration when they would not "work" the first several times. As an instance he cited Dow's stubbornness as a boy in sticking to the job of inventing a thermostat for his homemade egg incubator till, on the fortieth try, he came up with one that actually worked. The point of this was of course that there were processes at Midland which had resisted Herbert Dow's plans for them far more than forty times, but were now performing very tractably indeed.

It could be said that the chemical industry had come of age in Herbert Dow's lifetime, and with a good deal of help from him. It fell to Dr. Barstow, as another associate of long standing, to review in detail some of Dr. Dow's contributions to the industry. These were of two sorts, and many instances of each were mentioned.

In one group fell Dow's *specific* accomplishments: things like the introduction of cheap phenol; the creation of a steady domestic source of metallic magnesium; the breaking of foreign monopoly in chemicals like bleach, indigo, and the salicylates; the development of carbon tetrachloride as a volume end product and as a starting material; the development of chlorine as a cheap and widely used processing material; the finding and developing of more and more uses for bromine, and so on. In 1900 The Dow Chemical Company was a small concern manufacturing two products, potassium bromide and bleaching powder; in 1930 it was an aggregation of plants manufacturing 800 freight carloads a month of 150 different chemical products.

Into the second group of Herbert Dow's contributions fell many that might be called *general*. Here Dr. Barstow emphasized Dow's pioneering and development of the continuous process, automatically controlled and operated; the constant search for new processes and products; the exploitation of previously unwanted by-products; the teaming-up of chemical and engineering skills to make products more cheaply; the determined exploitation of such inexpensive raw materials as brine; the commercial importance attached to research; and, perhaps above all, the sheer *creativeness* of Dow's industrial attitude.

Obviously, Dow had not been the only man to bring such ideas and practices into the industry, nor was any claim made that he was. The point was that Dow had been among the very first to introduce them, and had been so successful with them that they necessarily became standard practice throughout the industry. It was these things that had brought the industry of age and made it the aggressively *creative* activity it has been ever since; and thus it was that Dow's pioneering of them had developed not only his own company, but stimulated the development of the entire industry.

For these and other achievements Dow was presented the medal and asked to speak. He was then in his sixty-fifth year, and sicker than anyone but he himself knew of the ailment that was presently to kill him. It would have been understandable if, in response to the recognition given his life-work and character, he had become emotional and reviewed his struggles and defeats and triumphs. Instead, after a word of thanks for the honor bestowed on him and through him on his colleagues, he launched into a businesslike discussion of what he knew the assembled chemists would like to hear—techniques he and his colleagues had worked out for lowering costs and increasing production. He traced the growth of the industry from the old small-batch method to the massive continuous process, automatically operated. He pointed out how chemical after chemical had thus been made cheaper and more plentiful, with the result that more chemical products could be made and sold, more people employed, more money earned, and more people benefited. In a word, he showed how industrial chemistry had begun to do what it has been doing ever since—create more and more of the comforts and necessities of life and put them in the range of more and more people.

In the few months of life which remained to him, Herbert Dow had the satisfaction of seeing a number of long-range projects which were to be very important in the company's future show the kind of promise he had hoped for them. Magnesium metal, for the first time in the company's history, was paying its own way. Enough test runs had been completed to show that bromine could be taken at a profit from sea water. An ammonia plant had been completed which used by-product hydrogen to give the company a tremendous supply of cheap ammonia. Much of this ammonia was used to replace the more expensive nitric acid in the manufacture of aniline. This gave the company a vast and cheap supply of aniline, and aniline products in volume began pouring from the plant. Another important advance of this time was the perfecting at Midland of a highly successful process for getting such unsaturated hydrocarbons as ethylene, propylene and butadiene from petroleum. This development was to prove one of the major milestones in the field of petroleum chemistry, which was just then opening up on a grand scale; and from it stems The Dow Chemical Company's present pre-eminence in the field of plastics, solvents, synthetic rubber, and other triumphs of modern organic chemistry.[1]

Knowing that such things were afoot, it is not hard to get the point of a remark Herbert Dow made to a colleague at this time. "I imagine," said Dow, "that they're wondering around here what will happen when I'm gone. Well, they've got plenty of work lined up for them."

Incidentally, though he personally was the wellspring of many of the company's most successful ideas, and had a great deal to do with making many of them work, Herbert Dow never looked on himself as indispensable

---

[1] Such developments have exceeded even Herbert Dow's imagination in scope and massiveness, and have had much to do with increasing the company's productivity tenfold within twenty years of his death. The point here is that they were begun in Herbert Dow's day, often before the industry as a whole was interested in them, and very often indeed after many years of trial, error, and frustration.

to his company's progress. What he did consider indispensable was the attitude of *enterprise* he had built up in his colleagues—the attitude of willingness to try anything that *should* work and *make* it work. That attitude is to this day probably the greatest single motive force in The Dow Chemical Company.

By the autumn of 1930, Dow was so ill that his physician was finally able to persuade him to go to the Mayo Clinic for an operation which might prolong his life. He died, and a special train brought him back for burial among the townspeople with whom he had worked all his life. One of his last official acts before going to the hospital had been to send for the foreman of an employee who had been with him from the beginning, and who had now grown old. When the foreman arrived, Dow was sitting looking out of the window. He glanced around, mentioned the old employee's name, and added:

"I don't want anything ever to happen to hurt his feelings."

Then he looked out the window some more, as if thinking of the old times. There was a long period of silence, which Dow finally broke by saying slowly:

"That's all. But remember, I don't want anything *ever* to happen to hurt his feelings."

Things like that are not posted on factory bulletin boards. But the human feeling behind them cannot be concealed, especially when there are a great many of them; and this may account for the reception given the train bearing Herbert Dow's body when it arrived in Midland. The day was rainy and cold, and the train very late, but practically every man and woman in Midland was standing silent at the station and along the tracks. No one had suggested this: the people were just there. Herbert Dow had achieved something that few men achieve, in industry or anywhere else—worldly success combined with the affectionate esteem of the people who knew him as he actually was.

But it is one thing to esteem a dead leader, and another to prove worthy of having been led by him. This now became the business of all ranks of the team he had built up. Led by Willard Dow and other men he had trained, the company was in the next two decades to increase in size and usefulness beyond what even Herbert Dow may have hoped for. The Midland operation grew very much larger; there are now also major Dow plants in Texas, California, Oklahoma, Connecticut, and Canada, and sales offices all over the country. This can, of course, be called "expansion"; it would be more accurate to call it "development." And practically all of this development has been along the general and often also the specific lines mapped out by Herbert Dow.

Shortly after his death, a magazine which does not often praise businessmen praised him as "an old-fashioned free-enterpriser, creative, independent, dogged in purpose." To the extent that an epitaph can fit any man whose spirit lives on as his does, that and the silent crowd at the railroad station can be Herbert Dow's.

(ɪ)